to tent. But mostly the Japs were taking it easy in the heat of the day, no doubt resting up for a night foray of some strength. Under a spreading broadleaf tree perhaps fifty men were lying on the ground, talking, smoking, and sleeping.

"Golly!" Sheldon whispered. "Did you *know* they were here?"

"No, I didn't know it, but I thought they might be. Swell place for a hide-out camp."

Wermuth's eye quickly took in the scene. He estimated the bivouac to contain at least five hundred troops. Slowly he backed away from the cliff, the two men following. They went into near-by cover on cat's feet, and Wermuth sat down. Taking a sheet of paper and a pencil from his pocket he hurriedly scribbled a few lines about range and direction which he gave to the Filipino Scout.

"José," he said, "get this to the battalion major. Present my compliments and tell him I suggested a few rounds of 155's would clean up this ravine in fine shape."

"Si, captain—me voy." The lean brown lad took the paper, saluted, and was gone in the jungle.

"That boy's the best runner in the outfit," Wermuth said. "He'll be at headquarters in half an hour. And then—oh, boy, but this is going to be good."

"Artillery?"

"Bet your life. We've still got some artillery left and it is good. They'll blow all hell out of this camp."

The minutes dragged, while the two men talked of this and that in low tones. The only sound they heard from the Jap camp was a rattling of tinware, as though some cans were being moved. For the rest all was silence except for the call of a bird high above in the trees. The sector was quiet.

"Too damned quiet," Wermuth allowed.

Then, from somewhere far off the two straining men

heard a boom. Seconds later came a thin whistling sound that mounted instantly to a screech high above them, then dropped into a diminishing wail. And then the very earth under them shook with a roar from the near-by ravine.

"On the nose, by God!" Wermuth spoke aloud now.

This time the two men heard no far-off boom, but merely a series of rumbles like distant thunder. Then came the whistle and the scream of shells, and mighty explosions filled their ears with terrific sound while the rocky ground quivered and shook as if by some convulsion of nature. Shell after shell came over to fall in the ravine, and up out of the ravine now rolled a great column of smoke.

The shelling stopped as quickly as it had begun. Up and on his feet Wermuth rushed the short distance to the cliff, took a quick look. It was the greatest shambles he had ever seen. Smoke still lazing prevented a complete view, but he saw enough of blasted tents and shacks and earth and men to know that the shelling had been as murderous as he could have wished. He ran back to Sheldon.

"Nice shooting," he said. "Lovely slaughter. Now let's get out of here."

They started back toward the American lines, hurrying to get away before Japs could swarm in from all sides to see what the shooting had been about. But the two men didn't make it that easily. They walked head on into a patrol of six Japs led by an officer. Quick as a wink Wermuth shot the officer and the soldiers scattered into the jungle. Holding his tommy gun ready, Wermuth was surveying the field for more targets when something told him to turn around. He did so. The supposedly dead Jap officer was on his feet, tugging away at his Nambu automatic pistol which had stuck in its holster. Wermuth upped with his tommy gun— but it was empty. He carried no sidearms.

"Sheldon, quick! Cover this guy," Wermuth shouted. The Marine came on the run, pulling his revolver to cover the Jap officer who threw up his hands in surrender. He was game enough, this Jap, but his gun had stuck.

"Let's take him back as a souvenir," Wermuth suggested. So, helping the wounded Jap along they returned to Fifty-seventh Headquarters.

Two days later Wermuth played in bad luck for a change. He had scarcely left camp on a little trip alone when an enemy sniper shot him in the leg. He bound up the wound and hobbled back to camp disgusted and somewhat irritated. "These goddam snipers are becoming a nuisance to all of us," he complained. "I think it's high time we did something about it. They're bothering us constantly."

The Jap snipers on Bataan were better organized than any other snipers before them. Each carried a hood of green cloth and mosquito netting that covered the helmet. Sometimes he stained his face with leaves or paint. He had a coil of stout rope to aid in climbing trees and tying himself to branches. In his equipment, which was surprisingly light considering, he carried food, drink, quinine, first-aid kit, an antidote for mustard gas, a gas mask with spare lenses, a can of chlorine or some such substance for purifying water, extra socks, a toothbrush, and gloves. Many if not all snipers also had a neat job of a flashlight with rotating bull's-eye of several colors, to be used for signaling purposes.

The sniper's food consisted of rations for five days—a small bag of hardtack, a five-inch sack of rice, half a pound of rock candy, a package of food concentrates, a small can of coffee, and a box of vitamin pills. With such equipment, the Jap sniper, used to low nourishment anyway, could carry on for a couple of weeks if he managed to pick up a bit of extra food in the jungle, which was not difficult even at the height of the fighting.

As Captain Wermuth nursed his leg he became more and more irritated at the thought of these snipers. He

formed an antisnipers' association with the avowed purpose
of cleaning up the local situation. Eighty-four of his beloved Philippine Scouts volunteered. They'd follow this
guy, this One-Man Army, as he was coming to be known,
anywhere. Before dawn next morning the Bataan Antisnipers' Association went into action.

Between dawn and half-past eight the boys accounted for
an even dozen snipers, all of them shot out of the branches
of big kamachile trees. Keeping to their busy work every
morning, the "Association" managed in less than one week
to bring down two hundred and forty-three snipers and also
wiped out two Jap machine gun nests.

This kind of war, this war on Bataan Peninsula, was the
sort that never bogs down into war of position, such as the
Western Front was in the first World War. This was a war
of movement, constant movement, the kind that livens Civil
War history between sieges, the kind the Green Mountain
Boys fought in the New Hampshire Grants, the sort of war
Major Robert Rogers liked to wage with his Rangers. And
it was a war made exactly to suit the disposition and talents
of Captain Arthur William Wermuth. Presently he had, or
perhaps he made, an opportunity to add a new note to his
raids.

Wermuth is patently a man determined never to get in
a rut. He says that ruts play havoc with the imagination,
they dull a man, tend to make him incapable of independent
thought and enterprise.

Keeping this idea in mind, he loaded five gallons of high-
test gasoline on his back one dull night in January, and
started out alone for the Jap-held town of Samai. He'd been
there before, in pre-Jap days, and he had little trouble
making his way through the night and the Jap sentries to
the edge of the village. All was silent in the sleeping town;
only the hard breathing of tired soldiers could be heard

as Wermuth put his ear against one of the shacks, which stretched in two long rows through the clearing.

Working fast but quietly he unloaded his gasoline, unscrewed the pouring cap, then walked down the two rows of buildings, putting the liquid where it would likely do the most good. Then he lighted a cigarette and threw the match. The gas-drenched shacks, dry from the Bataan dry season, leaped into blaze that mounted as Wermuth hurried away, gloating at the sound of roaring flames and the cries of scared and scorched Japs.

The thoroughly aroused town must have thought it had been attacked in force. Before Wermuth could get out of range, Jap artillery opened up from somewhere and he ran his first half-mile through a series of exploding shells. But he came through without a scratch. He remarked to some other officers what a fine morning it was, then went for some breakfast.

Incendiarism was good fun, Captain Wermuth admitted, but it didn't really amount to much. For the next several days he fretted away his time, lacking orders from above or any good ideas of his own. On January 17th, however, things perked up a bit. An American telephone line had been tapped by the enemy somewhere along its ten miles, and the colonel of the Fifty-seventh Philippine Scouts wanted something done about it.

This time Wermuth took his favorite Filipino noncom, the huge and willing and able Crispin Jacob, now a sergeant and mighty proud of his new chevrons. Sergeant Jacob stands—if stand he still does—6 feet 2 inches tall and weighs 210 pounds. He was a giant beside Wermuth who is about 5 feet 8 inches and stocky.

"Jock, we've got a dandy assignment today," Wermuth remarked as they left camp. "Those monkeys are tapping our wires. Many of them savvy American talk. The colonel says to go do something about it."

"You and me, we do something," said Sergeant Jacob who is not overly voluble. They started out to do so. Walking along the telephone line toward the Jap positions, they came to an open rice field, very dangerous to cross. Looking the situation over, they noted an irrigation ditch across part of the field. The two men crawled to its edge, and Wermuth rolled over into it.

He was, as he later admitted, surprised. He rolled over into the ditch and landed squarely on top of three Jap soldiers all intent on listening to talk over the wire which ran along the bottom of the ditch, and also operating a radio transmitting what they heard to Jap headquarters.

The struggle had hardly begun when Sergeant Jacob too rolled in on top of the others. He regained his feet first. "No worry, captain," he shouted, then stuck his pistol into the belly of first one, then a second of the Japs, firing each time. They dropped instantly. But the other Jap was free, free and fighting like a tiger. He rushed Wermuth with bayonet, cutting a big gash through the captain's arm just as Jacob stepped up and shot the Jap through the head.

The two Americans sat down for a few minutes while Jacob bound up the captain's wound. Then they picked up the dead Japs' equipment and returned to camp.

This time they managed to keep the wounded Wermuth in the regimental hospital for two whole days and three nights. Then he walked out without permission and directly into a new sortie, but not before a medical captain had taken him to task for disobeying hospital orders. "That wound isn't well, Wermuth," the doc said. "If you get infection in it, you won't be able to fight at all."

"But, doc," Wermuth protested. "You fellows fixed me up so good I'm as well as ever. See?" He flexed his arm muscles. "It was only in the flesh," he explained, as if the doctor didn't know. The medical man walked away muttering something about what-can-you-do-with-a-man-like-that?

The doc was right. You really can't do very much with a man like Wermuth. On January 19th, two days after the little affair in the irrigation ditch, Wermuth and five Marines volunteered to explode an incendiary bomb that had previously been placed in a cornfield for just such an occasion as the present. At present the cornfield was more or less infested by Jap ground snipers.

Well, on their way to the cornfield Wermuth and the Marines ran into a combination of Jap machine gun nests and trenches they hadn't known about. There ensued what Wermuth officially described as "a moment or two of fairly brisk fighting." One Marine was killed, two wounded. Wermuth and one Marine summoned help by another Marine, then attacked the nearest machine gun nests with hand grenades, and retired.

Captain Wermuth was considerably put out. The dirty Japs had prevented them from setting off that nice big incendiary bomb in the cornfield, hadn't they? "They can't do that to us," he complained, waving his arms.

Later that night American artillery pounded the cornfield unmercifully, while Wermuth with a score of Marine and Philippine Scouts got up close and dumped exploding stuff onto every square yard from trench mortars. The Japs withdrew, what was left of them, and the nice, big incendiary bomb was left within the new American lines. The Fifty-seventh took over the field.

Early in February an officer of the Fifty-seventh called Wermuth to headquarters and told him of certain information he would like to have. "And Captain," he added, "this time I want you not to get into any fighting. I merely want this information. It will be hard and dangerous enough to get without any fighting. Do you hear, no engagements this time?"

"Yes, sir, no fighting." Nor was there, this time. With four Scouts he advanced to the terrain which headquarters wanted scouted, made his observations, and was returning to camp when he sighted what looked to be a Japanese admiral's blue uniform. The man in it was wearing a sword and considerable braid and was apparently being guided on a sight-seeing trip by a Filipino civilian. Before Wermuth could stop them, his own Scouts, notoriously quick on the trigger, had opened fire. The blue uniform disappeared into near-by woods, sword clanking, but the civilian was taken prisoner.

When Wermuth reported to his superior officer, questioning brought out the fact that Wermuth and his party had penetrated far back of the Jap lines. The officer blew up. "I sent you on a reconnaissance trip," he exploded to Wermuth, "and not on an expedition to the Army and Navy Club in Manila to get a drink."

"I didn't realize, sir, we had gone so far," was all Wermuth could think of right then.

"Let this be a reprimand, Captain."

"Yes, sir."

By now the fame of Wermuth's exploits had spread all over Bataan wherever American and Filipino soldiers talked. He was emerging as the One-Man Army, and with some reason. His exploits already would, if they had been put into fiction narrative form, have been turned down as wholly improbable by the editor of the wildest and gaudiest pulp-paper magazine. Unofficially but very conservatively Wermuth was credited with killing (up to this time) ninety-five Japs, and of capturing "a score or more." Already he was a breathing, fighting legend, while he still lived, and he still had to add to that legend.

His next foray was a sudden affair, cooked up in a moment. The Japs were landing on Bataan's wild west coast. If they got a foothold there, it would be all over quickly with the hard-pressed Filipino and American troops. At the head of a group of volunteers, Wermuth attacked a company of Japs that had only just landed and were moving inland. This engagement developed into some of the most savage fighting the peninsula had seen. Attacking with rifles, pistols, grenades, and bolo knives, the assorted American force took on Japs that outnumbered them ten to one, slaying over one hundred and fifty and suffering heavy casualties themselves.

Next day Wermuth was back on the scout again, this time with Sergeant Jacob, the big Filipino. They were not supposed to be fighting this time, but only to get knowledge of where and how many of the enemy were landing or had landed in a certain sector. The two men were slogging along, "as peacefully as you could imagine," as Wermuth described it, when they walked fair into the range of a strongly fortified machine gun position. The Japs had seen them coming, too, and opened up. Wermuth fell from the impact of a bullet that shaved two of his ribs and came out through his back. Sergeant Jacob pulled him to cover and bound up the wound, which was bleeding much. Leaving his captain on the ground, the big lad filled his arms with grenades. He then flanked the machine gun nest, took his stance, and carefully heaved them one by one at the enemy position. Then he went back to Wermuth, who was attempting to stand but couldn't. Bullets were cutting the bushes overhead.

"I guess, Jock, you'll have to carry me this time," Wermuth said. Jock leaned over and smiled. "Captain," he said, "you easy to lug." He started to pick Wermuth up, then grunted and almost fell.

"You hit, Jock?"

"No, not hit. Only thought I was." The big lad rubbed his right leg a bit, then leaned over and picked Wermuth up as easily as if he had been a newspaper.

"You see, Captain, it's easy." Packing his captain on a shoulder, Sergeant Crispin Jacob, a glory to the Fifty-seventh Philippine Scouts, plodded two miles to field headquarters and directly to the hospital.

"Captain Wermuth got hit," the big man said, putting his officer tenderly down on a cot.

Wermuth was perfectly conscious. He sat up on the cot.

"Take a look at the sergeant's leg, doc," he said. "He tried to cover up but I damned well know he's been wounded." They tended to Wermuth's wound, and they looked at Sergeant Jacob's leg. Two machine gun bullets had gone through his right thigh, missing the bones by a fraction of an inch.

The doctor was astonished. "How did you manage to walk two miles on that leg and pack the captain too?" he wanted to know.

"Just as easy as could be," the Filipino said, and showed his white teeth in a big smile.

By mid-February both Wermuth and Jacob were out of hospital and looking fit for more trouble. Clark Lee, the Associated Press's able correspondent on Bataan at that time, saw them both and talked with them. Captain Wermuth told Lee that he felt certain no Jap bullet would ever get him for keeps. "I'll be seeing my wife in the States again," he said with certainty. "And I want to arrange for Jock—Sergeant Jacob here—to attend a military school. That man will make a great officer."

That's the way it went with Captain Arthur William Wermuth of Bataan Peninsula—the One-Man Army, the Rough-on-Japs Guy. He was decorated with the Distinguished Service Cross for extraordinary heroism, the Silver

Star for gallant conduct in action, and the Purple Heart with two clasps for wounds received.

How it goes today with Captain Wermuth is something millions of Americans, including his wife, Mrs. Jean Wermuth of Traverse City, Michigan, would like to know. When the ragged, starving Americans were forced to surrender at Corregidor, they slipped out of American existence as if they had been removed to the never-never land. They still live in honor and legend, none of them more so than Captain Wermuth.

Some day, perhaps in a year, perhaps in a month—for if Captain Wermuth is a prisoner he is likely to be hard to watch—it may be possible to bring down to date the saga of the One-Man Army of Bataan. It is sure to be hair-raising. Wherever he was between mid-February of 1942 and the fall of Corregidor, you may be certain that things were moving, going on, being done. He is a man eminently fit to sit beside the great informal heroes of America's past.

"Tell the men to fire faster and not to give up the ship. Fight her till she sinks."

COMMODORE JAMES LAWRENCE,
OFF BOSTON HARBOR, 1813.

2

THE CRUISE OF THE MARBLEHEAD

For EIGHTEEN YEARS the United States light cruiser *Marble-head*, third of the name, lived a sedate and uneventful life. She collected barnacles sedately, had them scraped off just as sedately, and on occasion she attended a mildly exciting Fleet Week in some American port. Launched in 1923, she seemed destined to finish her life on the scrap heap, with no great moments behind her that could be used, as in the case of the old *Constitution,* by a young Boston poet to save her from the ghoulish wreckers.

Then, suddenly on February 4, 1942, the *Marblehead* saw in three tragic blazing hours more battle than most ships ever know, and topped it off with a three months' wallowing cruise that is assuredly one of the great epics of the sea.

Captain Arthur Granville Robinson, late of Brooklyn, New York, was on the *Marblehead's* bridge that morning. His ship was part of a striking force standing off Balik Papan, Borneo, to ambush a large Japanese armada reported in the vicinity. American and Dutch ships made up the Allied fleet which was in command of a Dutch admiral.

At about half-past nine that morning Captain Robinson and other ship commanders got warning that a sizable flight of enemy planes was on the way to attack. Gongs rang. Men went to battle stations. Decks were cleared. The snouts of anti-aircraft guns lifted expectantly. Twenty-eight minutes later the first wave of Jap planes came over, thirty-seven of them.

Harold Partin, first-class machinist's mate on the *Marblehead*, had stood the 4-to-8 watch that morning, and at half-past nine he was sound asleep in his bunk. The gong roused him, and he heard his chief, Machinist Elliot Annis, shout: "It's a real raid, boys. Get going!"

Partin went to his battle station, which was the repair room amidships. He saw the first run of the bombers glinting in the sun. They slanted down and dropped their loads, while anti-aircraft and machine guns started to roar and chatter. The first stick of bombs meant for the *Marblehead* was wide—away to hell and gone off port, but they sent up spumes of water so high that other ships were lost to view.

Captain Robinson was maneuvering his ancient ship as well as he could, running a snake's course to dodge the bombs. The old machinery was put to top speed for the first time in years, and the engines pounded and racked and shook until the ship vibrated in all her parts. The *Marblehead*, built back in the days of Harding normalcy, was no greyhound. She was not constituted for dodging bombers, nor was she heavily armored. A hit would likely sink her on the spot.

Now a second flight of Japs came in for the run. This time they laid them right down close to the trembling light cruiser, while all those who could see the bombs coming dropped flat on the deck. It was what is called a near-miss, an ambiguous term that fails to cover the situation. What happened was that the second stick of bombs dropped close enough to the *Marblehead* to raise her high out of the water, and men on her decks thought they were looking through the streaming veil of Niagara Falls. All they could see was water, a gigantic screen of it that seemed to reach the sky.

That's how a near-miss looks to a man who has been near-missed. The old ship heaved and shook mightily. "She seemed to heel almost over," Machinist's Mate Partin remembers. When she sank back from the explosion to relax, her sailors could hear her very bones creaking and groaning. Word immediately went up to the bridge from below: "We are taking water through the seams, sir."

The cannon in the turrets and the machine guns along the decks set up a heightened clamor. The third flight was on the way—they were nearing now and the gunners were turning loose with all they had. Partin and his fellows saw the planes, saw them slanting down, saw the bombs coming. "A nervous moment," Partin says. He threw himself flat on the deck as the bombs struck, this time no near-miss but a fair hit, aft—yes, and another fair hit forward.

The concussion of that blow was something men may feel but not describe. There is no common experience by which to describe it. It shook Partin and the others as if thunder held them fast.

Flame rolled up high before the ship had ceased to shake. Black clouds of smoke instantly followed.

"Group Five forward to fight fire." Partin and his crew of five went forward as fast as they could. It wasn't any too fast. A bomb had ripped a great hole in the deck. They had to crawl over and under and through huge pieces of steel that were now twisted into the patterns of a horrible dream-world—barricades such as one meets in nightmares, seemingly impossible to pass, and mocking in their intricate patterns.

Twisted and stuck into this barricade, jammed into corners, and impaled on deck machinery were recognizable parts of what had recently been men, American bluejackets, good men all, now fit only to be collected and to be buried, when time allowed. The deck was awash with the sea and slippery from the blood of these brave boys. Somehow, Partin and his gang got through. They found the forward fire pump still in working order. They strung out the hose and turned on the water. Other crews were fighting the flames with the steam from ruptured pipes. In one compartment men let go a tube of carbon dioxide that quickly stemmed the local fire.

Meanwhile some of the firemen and other volunteers were searching out the wounded and the dead, lugging them from all sorts of hellish holes to the open deck, where they were laid in rows—yes, rows, for the dead numbered fifteen and the wounded a score. Medical Officer Frank Wildebush and his aides, working with scant supplies and crude equipment, began a stretch of work that was to last forty-eight hours without remission.

Another wave of bombers came in on the run. They scored another hit. The ship's great shudder threw men to the deck, some to stay, and the port side burst into flames. The fire was now reaching up high in sheets. Smoke mushroomed from new places. Men could scarce see what to do next, or even what they were doing.

This hit knocked Captain Robinson to his knees, and likewise the steersman. A second later the man at the wheel reported the steering gear gone.

Shift was made to the auxiliary steering apparatus. It was gone, too. The rudder had jammed hard over. The ship began to run in a circle, a circle marked by the bomb splashes as more Japs came over to unload. Now it was steer by the propellers, first one, then the other.

As if the sorely hurt ship and her crew needed more troubles, a new one promptly came to harass them. The 50-caliber ammunition began streaming out one of the gaps in the ship's side. That was bad enough, but the sea was pounding into the magazine where the 3-inch shells were stored. These babies with their war heads all set and ready could blow the ship to kingdom come from the inside. All that was needed was the detonation of one shell; the others, in the manner of shells, would follow.

Men were somehow spared from other work to handle this newest menace. From three decks down—it seemed to the crew the deepest decks they had ever seen—the cases of potential extinction were passed up, hand over hand, ladder after ladder, to be stored in a safer place—if there was any such.

Bad news continued coming from below to the bridge every second. The *Marblehead* had great holes in her sides. The sick bay and most of the medical stores had been blown away in that second blast. Water was pouring into the forward bottom. Into the aft bottom. The fires were spreading.

Captain Robinson remained calm throughout, giving orders at split-second intervals. When he saw the fires mounting, spreading, lapping out afresh, he knew he must act quickly to save the ship from blowing up internally. "Get rid of the gasoline stores," he told his executive officer. They sluiced it, barrels of high-test gasoline, over the side, and the sea around the *Marblehead* lighted up instantly, burning away on all sides, casting a bright glow through the smoke.

The Dutch admiral had seen the plight of the *Marblehead* and gave her up for lost. Now he sent two Dutch destroyers alongside, and one of their commanders told Captain Robinson: "We are standing by to take off your crew."

The Old Man of the wounded and flaming cruiser waved them away. "Thanks," he shouted through his megaphone, "but I'm going to put her through as she is. Stand away." The Dutch ships drew off, but started zigzagging through the burning oil to break up the flames surrounding what the Dutchmen thought was a doomed ship skippered by a crazy captain.

Machinist's Mate Partin and his boys were still pouring water onto the fire on the forward starboard side, and they got it out in an hour and a half. Now they shifted to help the firemen on the port side.

But the battle wasn't over yet. Again the Japs came, this time to ignore the *Marblehead*, which they doubtless thought sinking, but to plaster other ships in the fleet. Meanwhile, Captain Robinson's men were fighting their ship to the skipper's taste. The *Marblehead's* turrets and all her gun positions were shaking and shivering from the recoil of the anti-aircraft and the machine guns. Flames blazed out from aft and forward. These gunners were shooting for all the weapons could stand. They winged a Jap plane, they shot holes in others, once they were sure they had sent a Jap into the boiling, smoking, raging battle sea.

Down on the inside of the *Marblehead*, Chief Bosun Harvey Anderson and his crew were working madly to keep as much of the sea out of the ship as possible. They plugged holes with screens, with planks, with any old debris they could lay hands on. They helped men out of the lower handling room, where water was beginning to flow in an ever-greater stream. They dogged down the hatch, shored it shut against the rising water beneath, and knocked home the wedges with sledge hammers.

Up on deck Commander W. B. Goggins, second in command, had been wounded and badly burned. He pulled himself to the bridge and was ordered below. Commander Nicholas Van Bergen, gunnery officer, took over for Goggins. He seemed, men said, to be all over the ship, pulling sailors away from death by smothering in oil, from drowning; seeing everything, reporting all to the bridge, quick but calm and cool as ice. Mate Partin thought how swell a big dish of ice cream would be, or a drink of ice water, or a drink of any kind of water that wasn't salt.

Elsewhere on the reeling, wallowing ship Martin Moran, first-class metalsmith, and a ship fitter were engaged in a serious job. The rudder had been jammed hard to port. Nothing normal could budge it. The ship could move only in a groove directed by the rudder. The thing would have to be cut loose. So the two men were lowered deep into the *Marblehead* and there cut the chains, while the sides of the ship rocked from bomb concussions and oil and water leaked all over them from sprung seams.

In the galley the ship's cooks were making coffee with the last fresh water on board. They fed the crew what they could find to cook—stuff without bomb fragments in it— then they turned to help the doctors, to fight fire, to do anything that needed doing. Among the galley crew were several Chinese, and the Americans swore they had never seen better workers nor braver men.

Lieutenant Commander Martin Drury, navigation officer who was also in charge of damage control, apparently was two men, maybe four. Crew members insist they saw him simultaneously at four different parts of the careening vessel. His assistant, Lieutenant Francis Blasdell, remained at his hot post in the central control station, maintaining communication with all parts of the ship despite smoke, heat, and rising water. The rising water was getting to be something. It mounted by the second. Blasdell stayed in his rat-trap room until ordered up, and by then there was only one way to go. That was through the leg—a narrow passage—of the foremast. Fireman De Lude, a hefty sailor, was nearest the opening when the order came to go up. He started through the hole, thought better of it, and backed out. "You guys better go first," he said. "I might get stuck, and look where you'd be!" But all made it through.

Outside, the Japs were still coming, again and again. They came for three hours on end. On one of the latter forays a Jap bomb crashed a turret of the cruiser *Houston*, not far from the *Marblehead*. The *Houston's* anti-aircraft, firing like mad, reached up into the sky and pulled down a Jap. Men on the *Marblehead* watched. They saw the wounded plane pull out of its first dip, then charge head on for the *Marblehead* in an attempt to crash it down, bombs, and all, on the cruiser's deck. But Commander Van Berger's gunners were ready. They turned loose a murderous concentration of fire on the approaching plane, literally shooting it into the sea, almost under the cruiser's bows. Had it landed on her decks, it would have been all over.

It looked as if it were all over with the old *Marblehead*, anyway. The steam lines were disrupted, so was most of the electrical wiring. The rudder hung limp. The decks were pocked with bomb holes, some of them chasms. The cruiser's sides were ripped, gutted. All sorts of necessary rigging had been shot away entire, or blown out of shape and out of use. The galleys now were gone. So was the sick bay, the hospital, and most of the medical supplies. But down in the hold, down there where tired, sweating men worked like redfaced gnomes to keep the wheels turning, the engines never stopped. They faltered now and then, while men held their breaths, but they never ceased to turn.

The two main fires started by bombs were got under control, which was more than could be said for the battered sides of the ship. Water was now coming in at an alarming rate. Those pumps still able to work at all were going at top speed, but the water was rising steadily.

"Man the buckets." That is the last desperate order that is given before the command to abandon ship.

Men who had been fighting fire for three hours, who had been patching here and welding there; gunners, messboys, all hands not needed elsewhere, turned to the buckets. From three decks down up the cruelly long way to the main deck, hand over hand, went buckets of bilge and oil and plain sea water. Men with puny pails attempting to keep the sea from swamping the Old Girl, their groaning, wallowing old *Marblehead*.

They bailed, said their officers later, like all the fiends of Satan trying to keep Hell from being extinguished. They bailed all afternoon and all that night. Men, spent beyond endurance, fell from the ladders, bucket in hand. Always someone was near to fill the broken link. Up, up and up— over and over again the buckets sloshed their way upward, spilling a little as they went, and down came the buckets again, empty now. Machinist's Mate Partin recalls it as perhaps the most grueling work they did that endless day and night.

But here would come Van Bergen, or Lieutenant Hepburn Pearce, or Bosun's Mate Herman Hock, or Chief Ship Fitter Hale McCulley, or maybe the Old Man himself, to tell the bucket brigade to hold on just a little while longer; that they were beating the water; that the pumps were working too. Just hold on. . . .

The bucket brigade never ceased. Men clung to ladders until their tough hands were blistered, and they could feel the ladder rungs in the soles of their feet for days afterward. Little wonder they did; they bailed forty-eight hours on end.

Captain Robinson had other problems too. With two great holes in the ship, both low and one well forward, he could not push the ship too swiftly or the sea would enter faster than all the bucket brigades in the world could bail. As it was, she was deep by the bows. Captain Robinson would have to be out of the range of the Japs by dawn, too, or they'd return to finish him off. Now that the rudder was limp and flopping with the sea, he could do some steering with his engines.

All praise to those old engines. They were built for duty, even in peacetime, and now they got it. Steering with engines is something like tacking. With one screw turning faster than the other, the ship would veer to one side and make headway; then they'd speed up the other screw and veer the other way. It's no great shakes as a method of travel, but it's the way Captain Robinson drove the *Marblehead* through Macassar Straits and into the Java port of Tjilatjap.

When they docked, the Old Man was still on the bridge, where he had been constantly for sixty hours. "I don't think there was ever a captain quite like him," says Machinist's Mate Partin. "In peacetime he was great. In battle, he is immense."

That day they buried the *Marblehead's* dead in Java soil, then they turned again to the ship, the ship that forty Jap bombers could not sink. She was a shambles inside and out. No wonder the two Dutch destroyers had stood by with the idea of taking off her crew. She looked, as some of the men remarked, like a spare bite for Davy Jones, virtually predigested.

There was no dock of any size in the little port. So they prepared her for patching in the manner of the days of old —by careening. It was piecemeal work. The tiny dry dock lifted one side of the bow partly out of the water, while the crew welded patches over her gaping wounds. Then they heeled her over and worked on the other side. They also managed to get her high enough to put a patch amidships. Then they let her back into the sea and climbed aboard. And she floated. It was a repair job done in a way that would have gladdened the hearts of Decatur and McDonough, and it showed that American sailors, now as in the old days, are masters of quick improvisation.

While the welders worked, others of the crew were getting

a supply of bamboo. They cut this up into long stalks, lashed them together, and called them life rafts, to take the place of the small boats and rafts that had been blown to bits during the three hours in Macassar Straits.

The rudder still flopped. It would have to wait. Jap bombers would be on the way to Tjilatjap any moment now, to prevent taking place exactly what had just been accomplished.

So the Old Girl, whom the boys were loving better every hour, again put to sea. The channel in Tjilatjap harbor is very narrow, hardly a lane, so a port tug took the cruiser in tow. She was an awkward vessel, this tug, and her awkwardness proved almost tragic. Just when she had got the cruiser safely through the channel, the tug accidently rammed her, making a hole below the waterline.

Possibly the *Marblehead's* officers and crew swore a bit, but they got busy. A ship fitter was soon lowered overside in a bosun's chair and he plugged the hole, not a large one but not to be left open to the sea.Then the Old Girl set out once more, this time heading for Ceylon, almost two thousand nautical miles away. She was still making water, but now the pumps were able to hold the leakage within reason. The buckets were never again used for bailing.

She made Ceylon without mishap, still steering a zigzag course by the alternating fast-and-slow propeller method. At a British port in Ceylon they found a dry dock large enough to berth her. They fixed her steering gear this time. They took on fresh water, a fair supply of food, what tobacco could be bought, and hit out again. By now the lads aboard were saying that the *Marblehead* simply could not be sunk, so long as Captain Robinson was on her bridge.

She left Ceylon just ahead of the Jap bombers. This time they steered, and steered pretty well, for South Africa, which was 4,376 miles by the shortest route. For several days the crew continued to live in filth and wreckage that they had had no time to clean up. Now they turned to the job of policing ship, below decks especially. Working in oily water up to their waists, often to their chins, they repaired and cleaned the flooded compartments.

Nor were they safe in sailors' snug harbor yet. Pounding down through the Indian Ocean they sighted a suspicious looking merchantman. The crew was ordered to battle stations. Gunners stood ready, hoping to God the stranger would break out a Nazi flag. The *Marblehead* spoke the stranger but got no reply. Captain Robinson maneuvered his ship into the sun, then ordered one shell across the stranger's bow. She hove to quickly and mended her manners. She was a British ship, London bound.

One more tragedy lay ahead. On the way down the southeast coast of Africa sewer gas developed in the bottoms of the cruiser. A ship fitter went to investigate. When he did not return in ten minutes, one of his mates went to find him. Neither came back. When this was reported to the bridge to Commander Van Bergen, that officer acted in a characteristic manner. He had a rope tied around his waist and was lowered into the evil-smelling hole. Flashlight in hand, he sighted a body. He grabbed for it—and passed out completely. They hauled him back up. It was as near death as he had ever been, even counting the three hours under the open sky that rained bombs.

The two unfortunate ship fitters were dead, and were buried at sea, the last casualties of the long voyage.

What cheered the boys most on the trip was listening to Jap broadcasts. Four times they heard Radio Tokyo report that: "The United States warship, *Marblehead,* and all on board have been sunk to the bottom of the ocean by our brave bombers." Every time the Japs told the story, it got better. Once the commentator added a few stirring lines of description, how the "sinking cruiser flamed until the sea had closed over it."

The *Marblehead's* boys heard these reports while they were bailing with buckets, when they were in the dry dock at Ceylon. And twice more as they plowed through the Indian Ocean. Always did them a lot of good and was the source of gags without end.

In a South African port, where excellent facilities were at hand, the crew made the Old Girl fairly seaworthy, then turned her toward home. None of the crew knew for certain where they were heading. But sailors know geography pretty well. They knew at what ports they had called. When they rounded the Cape of Good Hope, heading north and west, they knew their next port was likely to be on the Atlantic seaboard of the United States.

That's where it was and they brought her through the sub-infested Atlantic without so much as an incident. It had been a voyage of 13,500 miles, anyway you figured it, halfway round the world.

In dry dock on May 4, or three months to a day from the time they were bombed, the *Marblehead* as this is written is being repaired at what the Navy admits is "an East Coast port."

While repairmen hammered and welded, Captain Arthur Granville Robinson had a few words for visiting newspapermen. "The safe return of the *Marblehead*," he said, "is a tribute to the courage, the stamina, and resourcefulness of the American officer and bluejacket." Then he added a significant line about a subject to which the American public, given to extremely informal ideas of war, seldom thinks. "The *Marblehead's* return is also a tribute to the rigid technical training which prepared her officers and crew for the demands of war. The people of this country can well be as proud as I am of the courage and accomplishments of the *Marblehead's* crew. They were marvelous."

There will be a thousand footnotes, maybe ten thousand,

to the story of the cruise of the gallant old *Marblehead* and her gallant crew. I happen to know of one footnote at first hand. On June 22, 1942, in Seattle—a suitable place for it to happen—First-Class Machinist's Mate Harold A. Partin, on thirty-day leave from the Old Girl, and pretty, redhead Jacqueline Gibson were married.

Partin is a tanned and well-built sailor with black hair, green-gray eyes, a happy smile, and just a trace of the native drawl he acquired in Houston, Texas, where so many good bluejackets come from. When he learned, as he did on June 18, that the *Marblehead's* Old Man, Captain Robinson, was to be made a rear admiral, he all but wept for joy. "The Navy will never make a better or more-deserved promotion," he said.

When I last saw Partin he was heading back for "an East Coast port," ready to take his place again in the crew of the *Marblehead*, the grand Old Girl of the seven seas.

Work as diligently as we will, and with the best of heart, we lowly prose writers can do little but try to report the life and great moments of the *Marblehead* and her gallant captain and crew. It will take a poet to do them justice. *Old Ironsides* got a poem. So did the blundering *Hesperus*, not even a fighting ship, after she sunk on Norman's Woe. If poets are still practicing in the United States, one of them owes it to his country to do something right good for a ship whose crew will swear, either on a stack of Bibles or a copy of Bowditch, that she has the stoutest heart of any vessel that floats.

"... *beat them, or tonight Molly Stark sleeps a widow.*"

GENERAL JOHN STARK,
BENNINGTON, 1777.

3

LIEUTENANT WHELESS GOES BOMBING

Luzon had been the first objective, and that unhappy island seemed surrounded by enemy ships from which stocky yellow men were landing like an army of ants, moving rapidly but with studied precision inland to take up protective positions while field guns, mortars, medical units, and all the sources of supply were unloaded.

It was the first Sunday after Pearl Harbor, and the Island of Mindanao was under attack as well as Luzon. Those yellow men were coming in from the north, from the east and west, coming in planes from carriers, in transports and warships, swarming ashore through the surf, landing in parachutes. Was there no end to this horde of yellow ants?

A man watching from a hill above Legaspi Gulf, near the lower tip of Luzon, on that morning of December 14, could have seen still another part of the teeming Jap army making ready to land. Anchored close to shore or already docked and unloading was a flotilla of Jap transports, big ones, all packed to the rails with Jap soldiers and all the equipment for a huge force.

Some man watching did see such a sight in Legaspi Gulf early that Sunday morning. Whether he was on a hill, as he could have been, or in a plane flying high, which is also probable, was of no matter. He was an American and also a man of quick action. A few minutes after he had sighted the Jap armada his short-wave got word of it to American Headquarters. And an instant later American flyers on a hidden airfield on Mindanao, far to the south, got their orders.

The orders were of course in code. Decoding was the matter of two minutes: The squadron commander was to send bombers immediately to blast the landing forces. The location was given.

American planes of any sort were scarce in the Philippines in December of 1941. But this hidden airfield on Mindanao had five Flying Fortresses, B-17s, big four-motored ships. That was all it had—except for flying men whose knowledge of war had been limited to six days, with little or no combat experience. These flyers were for the most part untried, and so were their five bombers.

It didn't take long to get ready. Through the doors of each bomb-bay of the five planes went eight 600-pound bombs. Crews climbed aboard. Engines roared, and one by one the planes made their runs and took to the air, while the ground crews waved good luck and shouted messages for Japs that were drowned by the churning motors.

First to take off was Lieutenant Hewitt T. Wheless, twenty-eight years old, dark-haired, brown-eyed, slight and boyish in appearance, with an easy smile. Schooling at a military academy and the University of Texas had removed any trace of native Texas drawl; and he already knew how to lead and command men with never a rise in his voice.

The plane with Wheless mounted toward the clear sky as the second bomber roared down the field for the take-off. Soon the five Fortresses circled high above the field, then assembled in formation behind the squadron leader. Now they climbed.

The objective was near Legaspi, 400 miles away. As they pounded along just below the clouds, Lieutenant Wheless felt pretty good and so did his crew. This was to be a surprise attack. American fighter planes were to join the bombers to give them protection. It might not be a simple pushover, but it was going to be a surprise attack with fighter protection. No airman asks more. The Japs would be there at the docks, unloading men and guns. Suddenly the flight of heavy bombers would be overhead. They would unload, and that would be the end of these particular Japs.

"Just as easy as that," Lieutenant Wheless thought, or maybe he said it aloud, for his navigator Meenaugh said: "It's going to be fun to plaster those monkeys."

Half an hour later the flight ran into heavy weather. Pounding tropic rains beat on the ships, and clouds rolled together. Thunder shook the ships, and lightning played along the wings, while every part vibrated. The crashing black clouds around them made the noise of the planes seem dim, muted. The flight leader began climbing again, and now all were flying on instruments. At 14,000 feet Lieutenant Wheless noted that his Number Three engine was missing.

"What's the matter with Number Three?"

"Overheated, sir. It's out."

Wheless dropped his plane to 10,000 feet, while his crew worked on the dead engine. It coughed a few times, then went into motion again. But the other planes were out of sight.

Only one thing to do, Wheless thought, and that was to go right along to the target and drop the load. Maybe he'd beat the other four there, anyway.

Some fifty miles from Legaspi, Wheless dropped his plane again, this time to 9,500 feet. He was riding the top of a heavy cloud layer, hoping and looking for an open spot,

a place where he might see the ground and the bay. But
the all-enveloping clouds ran on without end. Sometimes it
seemed as if the clouds were racing the ship, keeping its
pace with ease and the crew blinded. But the target must
be near now, and Wheless would have to see it to bomb it.

Wheless suddenly saw what looked to be an opening.

"Prepare for bombing," he ordered.

The doors of the bomb-bay fell open, and the gear was
readied.

Just then it happened. The plane broke out of the clouds
and all at once they were in the bright sunshine of a tropic
afternoon. It was almost half-past two.

And what a target down there beneath them! Close to a
dock were four, five, six ships, Jap ships, all motionless,
something like an oil painting of six ships at a dock, blacks
and browns and whites against aquamarine, frozen there
on a canvas, silent, waiting . . . It was a picture Wheless
will never forget.

"All gunners to stations," he ordered.

Then to his bombardier: "Line up on them. We're going
in now on the run."

"Aye, aye, sir."

In and on the run they went, for that perfect target of
ships limned clear against the blue sea and the dark-brown
docks.

Just then the plane's rear gunner spoke through the
phone:

"Two squadrons of Jap pursuits coming along, sir."

"Which side?"

"On both sides."

"We're going in on the target, anyway. Open fire when
they're in range."

Might just as well get rid of the bombs, Wheless thought.
We came a long way with these bombs. Swell target, too. It
would be a pity to waste bombs, not to hit that target on

the nose. Out of the corner of his eye Wheless saw the first two Jap planes closing in, the Rising Sun insignia plain. He wondered vaguely where the other American bombers were, and also where the American fighters were. They hadn't come. But he didn't take his eyes off the target below, and now Jap bullets were coming through the fuselage. The American side gunners opened up at close range with their guns.

Wheless saw one of the Japs burst into flames, falter, then go rolling over and over and down, down. The other one disappeared too.

They were on the target now. Pretty.

"Bombs away," called the bombardier. "Bomb doors closed. Let her ramble."

Was it to be as easy as this? Two Japs knocked out, the bomb load delivered as ordered? Was that all?

It wasn't all. Two, four, six, eight—hell, ten Jap pursuits, all were coming after the lone American. Wheless made for a cloud, and looking down far below he saw great plumes of smoke and flame rising from the Jap vessels, and great plumes of water rising beside them. The bombs had fallen true, and wreckage of ships and bodies was now tumbling back into the harbor as the American took for cloud-cover, with ten—no, eighteen Jap pursuits on his tail.

Lieutenant Wheless's day was far from over. He guessed it now: that the other Americans had been there ahead of him. They had dropped their bombs, and gone on. By the time the laggard American had come over the target, Jap fighters were in the air like hornets. It was as hot a reception as an unescorted bomber ever received, and by now Wheless began to realize what sort of a party he had got into.

Diving and climbing by turns, in search of bigger and better clouds, the American was virtually surrounded by

Jap planes. Bullets ripped through the fuselage. They zipped through the narrow space between Wheless and his copilot. The Number One engine had been shot out of commission by the first burst of Jap fire. Wheless wondered if that cranky Number Three motor would hold. Number One was beyond help. But if three motors would function, Wheless figured he could make it, somehow, somewhere.

The Jap bullets had begun to do damage inside the plane. Gunners Killen and Williams changed places, Killen taking position at the "bathtub" guns in the bottom of the plane. A moment later Killen groaned and fell on his face. He was dead.

Up at the top gun, Gunner Williams was raining a steady stream of lead at the Jap hornets. He got two of them at once, maybe a third. They burst out into flame, then rolled over and went down out of sight, smoking. Suddenly Williams grunted, straightened up, then tumbled over backward. An explosive bullet had ripped up his flesh from knee to thigh, shattering his leg in horrible fashion. He struck the floor, then attempted to get up, to get up there to that gun again.

But he couldn't make it. That leg just wouldn't do to stand on, so he fell over on the floor, cursing his leg that wouldn't hold him up when he wanted to be held up and shoot, shoot. The gunner's pit was painted with splashes of blood.

Wheless was still looking for more cloud cover. Wasn't there any left? He managed to get into three or four scattered cumulus clouds, and the cover did some good; it gave the boys a chance to change their ammunition belts. But the cover would not last. He'd dive in, remain a moment, then they'd be out in swell shooting weather, with the Japs hanging close and tough.

With the Number One engine gone, the plane soon started to lose altitude. It was down from 9,500 feet to

Captain Hewitt T. Wheless

3,500 feet—and going lower. Bad stuff in such a place. Bad, bad. But the gunners were still shooting. Manning the guns first on one side of the plane, then on the other, the remaining crew kept up a constant fire, and Gunner Brown shouted: "There goes another of the sons of bitches!" Wheless couldn't see it, but Brown was right; another Jap turned over and went away, leaving a long trail of smoke.

Gunner Brown had a wristbone broken, but he never once went out of commission. He kept two guns going as if two unwounded men were on the job.

"It's queer about bullets," Wheless thought during these twenty-five minutes of assorted hell. "Killen and Williams change places. A bullet kills Killen in his new place, another bullet wounds Williams . . . Bullets sure are queer."

Just then Navigator Meenaugh came forward in the plane to speak to Wheless.

"What is it—?" Wheless began.

Meenaugh fell like a shot, landing down in the plane's nose, and half-a-dozen tracer bullets zipped through the empty space where he had been standing. He bobbed up again to tell Wheless the Number Four gas tank was leaking bad. "No, I'm not hit," he added, seeing Wheless's query.

Just as Wheless began to worry about the Number Four gas tank, he came out of a nice big cloud to see a mountain staring him in the face, dead ahead and too close for comfort. He gave the ship all she could take in a lift and a bank, and then the Japs came in again, firing from all guns. A bullet burned the side of Wheless's face and scratched it, and blood trickled down. Zip! Another bullet traced a pattern across his right hand, leaving a red streak and a bit of blood. Flesh wounds, both, but he had to keep wiping his face to keep blood out of his eyes. He needed his eyes pretty much.

Banking into a cloud and out again, Wheless was even

more surprised than relieved to find no Japs behind him nor above him nor in front nor below.

It was a relief, all right. But now Lieutenant Wheless felt very much alone. Not a voice could be heard over the phone or in the plane anywhere. The plane droned and droned, but it felt emptylike. Meenaugh had disappeared again after his dive into the nose and out. Was he dead? Was anybody alive? Wheless just didn't dare to pick up the microphone in front of him. He was afraid if he called there would be no answer. Could be no answer. So he sat thus at the controls, less glad that the Japs had gone than he was heavy of heart at the loss of his crew—all those good boys, the eight brave lads who had fought like hell.

After what may have been five minutes but seemed as many hours, up popped the head of the navigator, Meenaugh. "Want any help?" he asked.

"Boy! You sure look good to me." Wheless will never be happier in his life. "I thought everybody was dead," he said. "Go on back and see how the crew is doing. And take a look at the guns. Those guys may be back again."

"No they won't," Meenaugh replied. "They shot away all their stuff. That's why they went away." He moved back in the plane.

He found one man dead, three others wounded, one of them so badly that Meenaugh applied a tourniquet to the shattered leg.

The plane and its equipment were in pretty bad shape too. The radio had been shot away. One gas tank was still leaking a stream. All but four of the eleven control cables had been shot away. The oxygen system had been destroyed by gun fire—but that didn't matter much, for this plane would never get up high enough for oxygen again, anyway. Limping on three motors, it could barely hold to the 3,000-foot level it was now flying. Could it make the home field?

It was all Wheless could do to hold her level. Dark was

coming up from the ground, and now he could barely see the barricaded field where he was to land. He had no radio to tell the boys on the ground the condition his plane was in. Just as he got over the field, one of the three remaining engines went dead—out of gas. The big bomber rocked uneasily. Wheless was sure he did not have power left to circle the field while the barricades—put there to keep enemy planes from surprise landings—were taken down.

He picked up the microphone. "It's got to be a crash landing, boys," he said. He didn't want to try for a belly landing, for there was no way to strap down the wounded. It would have to be a crash.

On the last slant into the field, the plane hit a palm tree close to the barricade, sheering off the top with a crash that could be heard above the laboring motors. The plane rocked like a ship in heavy sea, then straightened, and Wheless let her down. The tires on the front wheel were flat, and there wasn't any rear wheel; it had been shot off entire. But Wheless let her down as easy as he could, and she rolled 500 feet with all brakes locked. Then she stopped short and went up on her nose.

The plane was home and Lieutenant Wheless found his legs very weak.

One dead, three wounded. How anybody remained alive was the mystery. A checkup next day showed some 1,200 bullet holes in the B-17. Every propeller blade had been hit from five to seven times. The Number Four gas tank wasn't present, nor was any part of the radio.

In a broadcast on April 28, 1942, President Roosevelt singled out Wheless, now a captain, and two other American heroes for comment. "I hope," said the President in closing his narrative about Wheless, "I hope that he is listening."

He was listening. With his young wife and baby daughter, he heard the commander in chief's words over a radio in Fresno, California, whence he had been flown from Australia.

The gallant fighting man from Menard, Texas (population: 2,375) was decorated with the Distinguished Service Cross by Lieutenant General George H. Brett, who took occasion to remark on the high courage and flying ability displayed.

The medal, the promotion, and above all the President's words over the air, telling one hundred and thirty million people that here was a hero, placed the shy captain in as fierce a spotlight as any man could have. Neither the spotlight nor the homage he has since received will ruin young Captain Wheless.

"Shucks," he told this reporter, and with no trace of synthetic modesty, "you and I both know that circumstances have a lot to do with things, especially in the making of so-called heroes. Any one of the eight men of my crew is just as entitled to all this cheering as I am. I just happen to be the one who was picked out."

There'll be no fathead about Captain Wheless. Soft-spoken, well educated, still boyish and unaffected, one would never guess, even through his eyes, that here is a man who was in as tight a spot as any. His early training, plus a tour as commander of a Civilian Conservation Corps camp in Texas, helped to make him shyly sure of himself. And when circumstances ganged up on him, he reacted in the fashion long held proper in his home state. The shades of old Sam Houston and Davy Crockett must be cheering for Captain Wheless yet.

"You may fire when you are ready, Mr. Gridley."

ADMIRAL GEORGE DEWEY,
MANILA BAY, 1898.

4

BULKELEY, THE PT BOAT MAN

TROPIC NIGHT HUNG HEAVY and quiet over the sea and the Island of Luzon as the crews climbed silently aboard two mosquito boats. Tide lapped at their hulls and flapped at the dock while Lieutenant John D. Bulkeley, commander of the squadron, explained the mission ahead of them.

The order was clear enough, and simple. It merely directed Lieutenant Bulkeley to take his two boats into Binanga Bay and to see what could be done about an enemy ship, class unknown, that had just arrived there under cover of darkness.

To realize the importance of these two small boats and the conditions facing them at this time, which was in late January of 1942, one should know that they were virtually all that was left of the American Navy in Manila Bay. The rest of the Asiatic Fleet had gone to Java and other parts, destroying the supplies left behind when the Yard at Cavite was evacuated. The mosquito boats, which Navy men call PT's—or patrol-torpedo boats—were as yet to prove their full worth. Many Navy men thought they didn't amount to very much.

Lieutenant Bulkeley had faith in his boats, in his little navy. Designed to run from 70 to 80 miles an hour, their engines already had done too many miles to be in top trim, what with no spares to replace worn parts. Today, or tonight rather, they might do 40 miles, or maybe only 35 miles an hour. Yet Bulkeley had faith. His tin-pot navy carried two torpedo tubes to a ship. The torp tubes were aft; to fire a tin fish the PT's must run in against the enemy, turn quickly, then let go while running away from their target.

Bulkeley commanded the squadron. His flagship was the PT-41, in turn commanded by Ensign George E. Cox of Watertown, New York. The other boat, the PT-34, was in charge of Lieutenant Robert Kelly of New York City.

Tonight, the mosquito boats' engines were tuned as well as their condition allowed. The covers of the machine guns were removed, leaving the small steel mouths ready to start their grim stuttering in a dialect that is readily understood by all nations. The tubes were packed with smooth, black-coated death. Hawsers were cast off, engines turned, and the two boats streaked away to turn from shadows into nothing in the ocean dark.

But Binanga Bay was dark only in spots and for brief periods that night, which happened to be the 19th of January. Searchlights on shore gleamed from Jap positions and swept the water in nervous eccentric arcs.

The foaming wake boiled past the bows of the speeding boats, leaving the telltale phosphorescent glow that might mark their voyage for the watching Japs, if the big lights didn't find them first. Twice the searching fingers swept over the leading boat but did not come low enough. Then they swept aft—still too high to catch Kelly's boat.

For twenty minutes the PT's kept their course without interference. Then the accusing eye from shore rested briefly on Bulkeley's boat, and passed on. All hands breathed easier, but too soon. The eye was returning uneasily for another look. On it came, sweeping the choppy sea, and now it caught the PT-41 and held it fair in the beam.

"It won't be long now," commented Chief Machinist's Mate C. C. Richardson. A moment later Jap shore batteries opened up with all they had. Fore and aft, on port and starboard, plume after plume of the sea erupted and rose high above the speeding boat. Shells screamed overhead. Even machine guns were spraying leaden hail, but in the PT's wake—so far. Meanwhile Lieutenant Kelly's boat was disabled. She made her limping way back whence she had come.

Bulkeley was sending his ship in speedy zigzags, keeping her nose in the general direction of where his quarry was said to be. In and out of the brilliant flashing light it sped, with shellfire following close but never hitting her. But where was the quarry?

"Enemy boat on starboard bow." The lookout called the news, and Lieutenant Bulkeley raised his night glasses. It was a Jap patrol boat, and before it could begin firing, the PT's 50-caliber deck guns were shooting. Bulkeley had no trouble leaving the patrol far behind.

On they went, with eyes straining through the dark to find what they had come for. They ought to be about there now. Another five minutes, perhaps ten minutes, and the sharp eyes of Benny Licodo saw something. Benny, the Filipino steward, had cat's eyes. "Ship ahead, sir," he called to the lookout, and the lookout, who had but ordinarily good eyes, had full trust in Benny's. "Ship ahead, sir," he repeated.

Bulkeley put the glasses on her. The PT pounded on, and presently the watching American could see something ahead that was looming up as big as a house, as big as a barn, no, as big as Madison Square Garden. Then he knew

he was running right at a Jap cruiser. He gave his orders:
"Ten degrees left rudder. Full head on the engines. Torpedo crew stand by."

The Jap warship loomed terribly large as the mosquito bore down on her, but Bulkeley knew that one of his fish could whittle her down to size. He gave a quick order. The PT boat swung in a sharp, sudden arc that stood everything aboard her almost on end.

"Fire one," said Bulkeley.

A long shape of sleek destruction leaped clear of the tube with a hiss of compressed air and splashed into the sea, then hurried on its robot way toward the hulking apparition.

The mosquito boat sped away, and the seconds passed with the PT's crew waiting, waiting, for the big noise. It didn't come off. The fish had missed. The sharp eyes, the almost miraculous eyes of Benny Licodo saw it miss.

Lieutenant Bulkeley wasn't going to leave things that way. He pulled his boat around and again he started for the apparition. But the hulking monster was an apparition no longer. Its deck guns were shooting, blazing away, sending big shells screaming too high over the mosquito. The PT roared ahead through big splashes as the Japs attempted to bracket her with their fire.

Bulkeley was now calling the figures he wanted set on the torpedo's dials and gadgets.

"Ready, sir," came the word from his torps men.

"Full left rudder," said Bulkeley. The PT went over on her beam ends in a spray that shut out for a second the blazing guns on the Jap.

"Fire one," ordered Bulkeley. The torpedo hissed, then splashed, and spun away. This time the tin fish went spinning with fury in its mechanism and destruction in its war head. A few seconds after the hiss, the crew of PT-41 saw a great blinding flash at the big Jap's bow. Then over the water came a mighty roar as tremendous flame leaped high to light the bay for a mile or more around.

The great roar, the mighty roar, died only to be followed in quick succession by other explosions. Now the big ship was silhouetted black against her own flames. She wasn't firing at the mosquito any more. Men were dropping down over her side. She was a goner, right now.

Lighter by tons now, with her tubes empty, the PT-41 sped away home in the light of a blazing warship.

Sending down the cruiser was not the first or the last of the deadly forays the PT squadron made against the Japs. On December 10 when scores of Jap planes were bombing the Cavite Navy Yard, two of the squadron's boats placed themselves in the raiders' path. As the bombers came down in their headlong rush, the turrets on the mosquitoes went into action, eight guns spouting a stream of lead into the planes. All three attacking bombers fell smoking and blazing into the sea.

Five days later, as the SS *Corregidor* was making her tortuous way across Manila Bay, she struck a mine near the fort and began to sink. Two PT's immediately put out into the Bay, threaded their way through the mine field, picked up 282 persons from the sinking ship and the water, and again made their way through the mine field to safety.

Sinking the Jap cruiser, though, had been the PT's great moment until the night of January 24. This one was even better than getting the cruiser.

With Ensign Cox again at the helm, Lieutenant Bulkeley took a mosquito out to Sampalac Point, at the entrance to Subic Bay, where a Jap aircraft tender had been anchored —incautiously, when John Bulkeley's gang was on the prowl. They had no trouble finding the Jap. They went in with their usual rush, made the turn-on-a-dime, and sent a torpedo crashing into the tender's midships.

The one fish doubtless was enough, but John Bulkeley is
a man who likes to make certain of a job. He ran his PT
to 500-yard range, then let go another torpedo. The crash
and explosion were magnificent, and the PT's crew got a
good view from their foaming stern.

Now a searchlight found the PT and played on her, and
from shore came 3-inch shells, howling overhead. It was
beginning to be time to get out of there, but Bulkeley didn't
want any Japs from the sinking tender to drown. He ran
in again, this time to within a hundred yards and then
turned his machine guns on the Jap. The sinking tender's
decks were alive with men, but only for a few minutes.
Twice the PT swept past, her 50-calibers rattling, sweeping the tender's sides, her decks, and the water around her.

It was, as the lieutenant later admitted, a most satisfac-
tory evening. "As I understand war," he said, "you've got
to kill the enemy, a lot of him."

The various raids of the PT fleet had by now roused
the Japs to furious action. Their patrol boats scouted day
and night. Planes came looking for them. But the Americans hid out by day in one or other of the countless bays
and inlets. On the night of February 1, one of the skeets
rushed to the west coast of Bataan where a Jap light cruiser
was landing troops. Two torpedoes struck the Jap. She
didn't sink, but she must have been badly damaged. She
raised anchor and went away.

For the next two weeks the mosquito squadron cruised
by night and hid by day, seeing no action. The crews were
letting their beards grow. Lieutenant Bulkeley's stiff black
whiskers did famously well. They burgeoned daily and
foliated until the boys said he looked more like a prophet
than a Navy man with four years of Annapolis behind him.
In truth, all but one of the skeet squadron's men appeared
very much like the sailors one sees in old prints of Civil

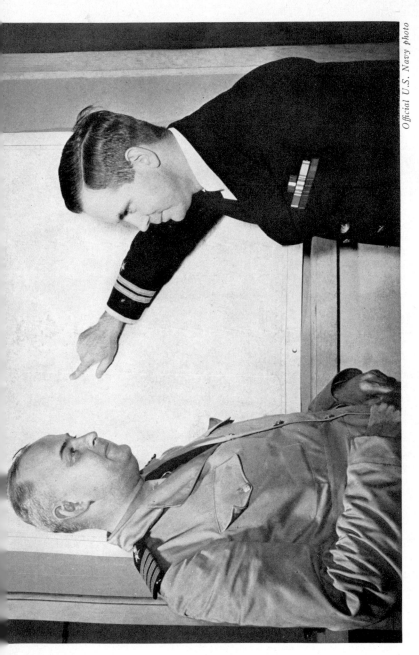

Lieutenant John D. Bulkeley (right) with Captain Leland P. Lovette, Director of the Office of Public Relations, Department of the Navy

War days. The exception was young Ensign Cox whose fuzz remained fuzz and who had to take a lot of horsing regarding his naked condition.

It was during this comparatively inactive period that C. C. Richardson, chief machinist's mate, kept the boys' spirits up by his elaborate wagers on the outcome of the war. Not the outcome, really, but *when* the Americans would win. His odds shifted almost daily, and seemed to be predicated on all sorts of unrelated subjects, such as the daily health and disposition of Boat 41's mascot, a monkey christened Admiral Tojo.

Things started picking up again on the night of February 18. Learning that a Jap tanker was moored at Olongapo dock, a PT went out with one torpedo and set the tanker afire. At almost the same hour in another mosquito, the beardless Ensign Cox sighted a Jap encampment. He cruised past once to take in the lay of the land. It looked like a pretty good opportunity.

Running his boat close in shore, and holding his fire until the figures of Jap soldiers could be plainly seen, Cox's boat opened up with its four machine guns, strafing the camp unmercifully for two hundred yards.

Three-inch guns on shore set up a clatter. Machine guns in the camp started spewing. And the quiet bivouac of the Japs turned into bedlam.

When he got to the end of the camp, Cox turned his boat on her heels and started back the same way. His four guns were blazing to the unheard but fervent profanities of joy of the American gunners. How sweetly they rattled! Enemy fire raked the PT, but she never faltered. Her engines pounded and roared as if they were never in need of new gaskets.

At the end of the encampment again, Cox shouted for a quick turn. "Let's do it again!" he cried, and sure enough they went right over the old route and shot away every bullet they had except a string for possible emergencies on the way home. But they got home without incident.

For three weeks the squadron lived in another comparative lull. Machinist's Mate Richardson, never at his best in such periods, allowed that he'd have to lengthen his odds if the Americans didn't get busy and do something. "This laying around will never get us anywhere," he said.

An opportunity for doing something arrived on the night of March 11. Lieutenant Bulkeley and his tiny flagship were ordered to a hidden landing on Corregidor. That night, which was mercifully dark, the boat waited to execute a very special mission, a mission then known only to Lieutenant Bulkeley. Just before midnight a group of Army officers, one woman, and a boy, came quietly to the dock and began boarding. Members of the mosquito boat's crew were both amazed and thrilled to see a tall, straight man with four stars on his shoulders.

"It's the General!" Benny Licodo, he of the sharp eyes, whispered. It was MacArthur with his staff, his wife, and son.

So, the PT navy was to carry the commander in chief on the first lap of his journey to the new front in Australia.

Hearts beat fast at the thought, even faster at the thought of the Jap shore batteries around Manila Bay. With all lights out the PT and its precious cargo pulled away from the dock.

"Full speed ahead," said Bulkeley, the boss admiral of the American fleet in Manila Bay, now engaged in ferrying the boss general of the American army in the Pacific.

Full speed was pretty fast. The PT had had some overhauling. Tonight she shook the full length of her seventy-seven feet from the pound of the engines.

One may ponder if any of the PT's crew thought of the voyage in relation to another time and another night, when "the fate of a nation was riding." Probably not. But fate was riding that night. Here was a small craft speeding through the night, speeding past the shore batteries of an alert enemy, carrying aboard the commander in chief of the South Pacific. It was a weighty load, no matter how you look at it.

On and on past the quiet batteries went the mosquito. Every moment the tightened minds of those aboard, especially the men of the boat's crew, expected to see a flash in the dark and to hear a shell on its way.

But not a flash was seen, either of cannon or searchlight; and two days later, on the mainland of the United States, millions of Americans felt better to know that their Number One man of the Pacific was safe in Australia. The mosquito boat didn't do it all, for a big plane took over at a secret rendezvous to finish the voyage. But the mosquito had the first lap and did it to America's taste.

By the time America knew of MacArthur's safe arrival Down Under, Lieutenant Bulkeley and his boys were planning another voyage. Back at Corregidor again, they stood by while President Manuel Quezon, his wife, two daughters, and his staff boarded the PT. It was to be the same thing all over again—that is, if the gods were with them still.

Choosing the same time of night and using the same cruising tactics, the boat set out to run the shore batteries. They did it again, and without seeing or hearing artillery. But a ghastly danger appeared much nearer than the shores of Manila Bay.

The sea was running high. The little boat was being slapped this way and that, like a mere chip. One of the boat's crew ran to Lieutenant Bulkeley to speak in a low voice:

"Sir, two of our torpedoes are loose. The retaining pins have broken."

Now John Bulkeley was a man inured to danger. He and his men had faced death from the sky, from the sea, from the land. He had seen several of his men killed. He had taken all these things in stride.

Here, however, was a new kind of danger, a horrible sort of danger, the kind a man couldn't stand up and fight against. Two deadly missiles, each twenty-two feet long—enough to blow not only a PT boat but a big battleship into pieces—were loose, alive, on one small boat. Bulkeley hurried aft to the tubes. He saw that the retaining pins, sure enough, were broken. The lethal cylinders were halfway out of their tubes, their grim mechanism set for action. A simple tap, a mere jar, in the right place . . .

Bulkeley later told a man that if he had had time to think even for an instant, he might have frozen with fear. But the sea was slapping the boat, it was slapping the two torpedoes. The boat and its cargo faced death in one mighty explosion that would have left nothing recognizable. If anything were to be done, it was now. And before Bulkeley could move further, it was being done.

Torpedo-man John L. Houlihan had run to the tubes, hammer in hand, and had started in. In a moment Bulkeley and two other men were at his side.

The four men went to work with an unhurried swiftness of motion that comes only from knowledge of the thing to be done and how to do it. Deluged by every wave that struck the boat aft, these four men went to work with hammers and gadgets. Each blow might be the blow to send them all to kingdom come, but the firing mechanism must be motivated. Hanging to the rail and the tubes for dear life, they struck between waves when they could see what they were striking at. Suddenly there came a great big whissh! and the two fish plunged into the sea and sped away . . .

One can wonder today, long afterward, if on some forgotten reef or shore are the two cylinders that might well have called for a new election of the Philippine Commonwealth-in-Exile and at the same time reduced Lieutenant John D. Bulkeley to a rank less than an ensign's.

The men besides Bulkeley who handled the "hot-run" torpedoes were John Houlihan, of Chicopee Falls, Massachusetts, already mentioned; James D. Light, chief torpedo-man, of Vallejo, California, and none other than the brave and able if beardless Ensign Cox.

With MacArthur and Quezon moved to safety, most of the mosquito fleet's men thought their part in the Philippines was over. Mate Richardson again took to complaining about lack of action. Again his odds on the war shifted erratically. Even "Admiral Tojo," the monkey mascot of PT-41, seemed morose. Then came the night of April 8.

The two mosquitoes were operating in the Mandano Sea near the Island of Cebu. Lieutenant Bulkeley still commanded his well-worn Number 41, and Ensign Cox was still at the helm. The other boat, the 34, still had Robert Kelly in command. Without any warning at all a flotilla of Jap warships appeared.

Bulkeley looked them over as well as he could. He found his two-skeet navy face to face with one heavy Jap cruiser and four destroyers. He blinked his aft lights at Kelly to say that he was going to attack and for Kelly to follow at the right distance. Then the two boats raced past the nearest destroyer and closed in on the big ship. Just then the cruiser's lights swept by and paused on Kelly's boat, paused and held it in the beam while the warship's secondary guns began blasting. It looked to be all over for Kelly.

Bulkeley ran his boat close to the cruiser, heeled, and let go. Right on his tail Kelly came tearing in, to turn quickly, and fire another torpedo. Both found their mark on the big Jap, which began smoking.

The Jap's guns were still firing, and Kelly's boat seemed to be in the middle of it. Barking out some fast orders,

Bulkeley raced his boat around the warship, hoping to draw some of its fire and thus permit Kelly to get in closer to loose another fish. Bulkeley got around the cruiser and in the face of gunfire from destroyers and the cruiser, too, he started sweeping the cruiser's decks with his machine guns. Just as expected and hoped for, the cruiser turned more of its guns on Bulkeley's boat.

While this maneuver was going on, Lieutenant Kelly saw his opening—and used it beautifully. Rushing in almost under the muzzles of the big ship's blazing guns, he let go a torpedo, dashed back on the return run, then loosed another. The two missiles struck the Jap with an explosion that rocked Kelly's boat like a cork. A moment later debris and Japs were falling back into the sea.

On the other side, one of the Jap destroyers was advancing on Bulkeley's boat, firing its machine guns and 3-inchers. The mosquito returned the fire, then ran away into the night, to hide near shore.

It wasn't quite all over yet. When daylight came, four Jap planes found Bulkeley's hide-out. They attacked at once, using both machine guns and bombs. Bulkeley maneuvered his boat very well and escaped, shooting down one of the enemy planes.

Kelly's boat had been badly shot up. He managed to get it to safety without help, then removed the dead and wounded. Bulkeley's boat was in little better shape, and all of its guns had been knocked out. Just before Corregidor fell to the enemy, the remnants of the mosquito fleet were destroyed to prevent their capture. Both Bulkeley and Kelly and their crews hated to treat their old boats that way.

Cox, Bulkeley, and Kelly were flown off The Rock just before it fell and were brought to the United States.

Lieutenant Bulkeley was pleased that the Navy gave him a Navy Cross and later the highest award of the nation

—the Congressional Medal of Honor. He was more pleased that the destructive ability of his PT squadron was recognized and praised by the Navy. He doesn't believe for a moment that PT's alone will win the Navy's war, but he thinks they are pretty darned good. Doubtless the Japs think so too.

John Bulkeley is a stocky, well-built man, with a good fighting face. His black hair is thinning. His blue-gray eyes are steady. Born in New York City in 1911, he was appointed to the Naval Academy from Texas in 1929, graduated with the class of 1933, and was honorably discharged. He got his commission in 1934. After serving on various ships he was put in command of a submarine chaser division in 1941. He used to live in San Antonio, but his wife, daughter, and son—the son born when father was sinking a cruiser—make their home in Long Island City.

Shortly after Bulkeley arrived in Washington after his exploits in the Philippines, Manuel Quezon came to town. Hearing that the hero of Subic Bay was back from the Islands, the Philippine president asked to see him, to thank him for taking the Quezons to safety. The smooth-shaven, boyish lieutenant was presented. Quezon was puzzled. He recalled a bushy black beard. "But I mean the senior Bulkeley," he said. "Doubtless the father of this young man."

"But," the Filipino was told, "this is the man who took you from Corregidor."

Quezon was amazed. "Had I known," he said to Bulkeley, "had I known you were but a boy, I should not have dared to trust my family with you that night."

Quezon's surprise made John Bulkeley very proud of that set of battle whiskers he had grown in the Islands.

"Damn the torpedoes! Captain Drayton, go ahead! Jouett, full speed!"

COMMODORE DAVID G. FARRAGUT,
MOBILE BAY, 1864.

5

THE VOYAGE OF HARLEY OLSON

THERE IS A FAMOUS PAINTING by Winslow Homer titled "Gulf Stream" which shows a lone and tiny boat, a mere dory, in an endless sea, and in the boat a lone man who is staring fixedly, with the fascination of horror and possibly of madness, at several leering sharks within arm's reach of the craft. It is a picture to chill the spine of the stoutest seaman, including that of Harley A. Olson of Portland, Oregon.

In April of 1942, Olson, twenty years old, blue-eyed, and over six feet tall, was radio operator on an American freighter plying the Atlantic, four days out of a United States East Coast port. He turned in rather early that night, which was the 19th, and he was sound asleep in his radio shack when the torpedo struck.

The jar woke Olson up but he did not hear the explosion. He noticed that his alarm clock had been knocked over. He turned it up and saw the time was ten-thirty-five. Just then the third mate stuck his head in the door. "Send your distress call," he said, "we've caught a fish."

Olson knew what that meant. He jumped to his radio desk. The generator had failed, so he tried to get the emergency radio working. For perhaps five minutes he moved the gadgets but could not get a reading on the ammeter. He sent a distress call, anyway, but knew it was very weak and probably would not reach anybody. It didn't.

Suddenly Olson realized that the ship was sinking fast. The floor of his shack, the deck, tilted at a crazy angle. Outside he could hear Captain Leonard Duks saying: "I'll see everyone off and into the lifeboats." Olson kicked off the slippers he was wearing and ran out on the starboard wing of the bridge. It was deserted. The night was pretty dark and Olson figured a storm was coming up. The sea was rough.

He couldn't even see the water and he couldn't know in what sort of a place he would land, but he dived off headfirst and as he hit the sea he struck some floating debris that cut a bad gash just under his left eye. The eye began swelling immediately. He started swimming away from the ship as fast as he could. It wasn't quite fast enough. He heard a crashing sound that seemed right behind him, a sound, he thought, that the collapse of a large building would make. He looked over his shoulder and saw the ship's bow high in the air, sticking straight up. He wondered briefly if he was away far enough to miss the undertow when the ship went down.

Floating things kept bumping him on the head. The infernal noise continued for another minute and now he knew what it was: The deckload of cargo boxes had broken loose and the boxes were tumbling, sliding, crashing, one over the other, into the sea. It was one hell of a noise.

The sea around him seemed to be as much debris as water, and Olson had to fight hard to keep his head above water and away from the bobbing, lurching boxes, big boxes that would knock a man out in a second if they hit him right.

He dived under a big crate and when he came up on the other side he had hold of a hatch cover. Never knew how he picked it up. He swam to the crate and hung on for a few minutes, getting his breath. The water was icy cold through a pair of khaki pants and a sweat shirt. Olson shivered.

Just then he sighted one of the ship's life rafts close by. He swam over and crawled aboard. He had never paid much attention to the rafts before, but now he looked this one over carefully. It was eight feet square and stood perhaps eighteen inches above the water. Olson knew the rafts were provisioned for fifteen men but whether for two weeks or four weeks he couldn't remember. His head had taken quite a pounding, and anyway it was hard to remember things past when so much seemed to be going on right now. He couldn't even remember much of anything except the third mate coming in and saying they had caught a fish.

Well, the ship had gone down now, and Olson wondered where the rest of the crew were. Had they gone down too? After a long time the dark seemed to thin out a little. Olson strained his eyes to see what was in his particular ocean. In the dim forerunner of dawn he could see little packages of something around him, floating by in droves. He fished one out. It was a package of cigarettes, pretty wet. He fished out another and another until he had about fifty packages on the raft. Figured the stock would last him as long as his food and water, anyway; but when morning came he found that the heavy seas had washed all but one package overboard.

As morning started coming in from the horizon Olson started to shout. He'd shout, then listen hard for a full minute. Only the wash and flap of waves on the raft answered. After several shouts he thought he heard an answer, and at just about the same time he was damned well sure he heard motors. The submarine!

It was the submarine. The throb of the motors became louder and louder. They were coming his way. Probably heard him shouting. He let himself over the far side of the raft from whence came the sound, got well down into the water and hung onto the raft with one hand. He was just in time. Swishing along through the twilight came the big sub, surfaced now, with men in its conning tower. They were talking but he couldn't understand a word. It was German, he was sure, but that was all. He lay low in the water until the sub was well out of sight and sound.

It was lighter now and the lone man saw that he was really alone with the sea. He swept the acres and acres and acres of waste around him with his good eye. Nothing. He dug a flashlight out of the raft's provision box and started to signal with it. Probably getting too light. He put the light away and looked up to see a raft near him. Gave him quite a start. But there was nobody in it, so he paddled over and tied the two rafts together. His thinking was all right again; he wanted to get the food and water from the other raft. Might be out here a long time. Back in Portland he had heard tales of that jinx ship, the *Dumaru*, which had blown up in 1918—the year before Olson was born— and how her crew had drifted in open boats from Guam to the Philippines, how they had become crazed for food and water, and how they had finally eaten the second engineer who died and . . .

Olson moved the provisions and water from the second raft to his own. Each raft had a ten-gallon can of water, he discovered, and some chocolate bars, malted milk tablets, graham crackers, and pemmican. He was cold and wet and tired and empty. He opened a can of pemmican, three ounces. He had never eaten pemmican before and he found it pretty good—at first. Tasted a little like a sort of fruit cake, he thought. What Olson really wanted, though, was a big platter of ham and eggs.

But hell, a man alone on a raft was lucky if he had anything at all. He chased the pemmican down with a drink
of water. Now he felt considerably better, except for his
injured eye which had swollen up as if half-a-dozen hornets
had stung him there. But he could see with the other eye,
and one was enough to tell him the ocean is a big place. All
around, as far as that one good eye could reach, he saw water
littered with wreckage, flotsam of this and that bobbing up
and down. The old ship had certainly held a lot of stuff. Too
bad to have it all drifting to hell and gone. The U. S. and
her allies could use it to good purpose. But there was plenty
more where that came from, and next time it would get
through.

Then his eye caught something besides boxes in the wreckage and he paddled over. It was a settee and he hauled it
aboard. Might as well be comfortable. But that wasn't all.
Along came another raft, one side torn off. Olson hauled it
close, tied it to his double-header, then prepared to transfer
the water and provisions. Those poor, pitiful men of the
Dumaru had drifted for how many days? Was it twenty
days or twenty-one days?

He found the provisions and moved them, but the water
can had jammed so hard he could not get it out of the
derelict raft, so he cut loose from the two derelicts.

The sun was up now and the warmth felt good. He knew
it would get plenty bright and hot a bit later. The pemmican had given him some strength, but even his strong
young limbs were still aching from the long swim and the
pounding. Now he dug a first-aid kit out of his stores and
patched up his eye. He dug out the distress flags each of
the three rafts had carried and prepared to make a sail.

The flags were bright-orange color and 3 by 4 feet. With
some safety pins from the first-aid kit he pinned the rags
together. He fashioned a mast from three oars and made
sail. It looked pretty fine up there, and he could feel the

tug of the wind on it. He knew he was in the southwest
Trades and that the wind was blowing toward shore. How
far shore was, he didn't know, but he guessed it at 300 miles,
maybe 400 miles. He was certain he would drift to shore
someday. He scanned the sea constantly that first day, for
expectancy was still high within him. He had seen in his
time many a ship come over the horizon and now, out here
alone, he thought every minute he'd see smoking stacks.
But he didn't.

Well, here was Harley Archie Olson of Portland, Oregon,
with a piece of the Atlantic all to himself.

He was using remarkably good sense. He had already
made such efforts as he could to better his physical condition—the orange-colored sail was flying as high as his
oar-mast would reach, he had stocked all of the food from
three rafts, all of the drinking water from two, he was
keeping a clean bandage on his injured eye, he had rigged
up a pretty fair bunk from the settee and some pieces of
boxes and a cushion fished out of the water. His body had
begun to break out in little boils which were uncomfortable
but he had rubbed some stuff on them he found in the first-
aid kit.

So, Olson started his voyage in good shape so far as the
physical properties were concerned. It was too early yet
to worry about going bughouse. Lone men on the sea had
gone bughouse, Olson knew that. He would take care of
the situation should it arise, but he didn't think it would—
not those first few days and those first few weeks. He was
in the shipping lanes. A vessel would be along anytime now.

It would be a good idea to keep a calendar, anyway, so he
scratched a mark on the raft every day. On the third day
he felt certain his lone voyage was over; on the horizon,
then nearer and nearer, came a ship. When it was about two
miles off he could tell it was a destroyer, probably an Ameri-

can, probably one that had ham and eggs and not pemmican
to eat. He shook his sails, he even stood up on his tiptoes
and shouted.

Meanwhile the warship disappeared. It was a disappoint-
ment, but not too bad. There were lots of ships on the sea,
moving around all the time.

Olson marked four straight lines on his calendar, then a
diagonal mark for the fifth day, and started a new series.
On the sixth day a freighter hove into view, but like the
warship she failed to sight the man on the raft. She passed
about two miles off and Olson thought he could smell the
aroma of ham and eggs a-frying.

Two more marks on the calendar. On the eighth day Olson
sighted a lifeboat with a sail up, heading west. It went right
along west. If there were humans in the boat, it was the
last sign of humans Olson was to see for a long time yet.

For an interminable time, a time that seemed to have had
no beginning, would have no end, and had no well-defined
divisions in it. True, night came, and then the broiling sun,
but they simply merged into Time—into Time, that queer
thing that runs forever on, that men mark into minutes,
hours, days, years, and punctuate with breakfast, dinner,
and supper, and Christmas and the Fourth of July, but
with which a lone man on a raft is helpless. Suddenly, one
day, it came to Olson that he couldn't remember if he had
made a mark on his calendar that morning. Had he? He sat
and thought hard about it for long periods. Sometimes after
that he would make a mark, and again he wouldn't.

A storm came up, an old rouser. It threw his raft about
like less than a chip. It washed away some of his gear and
he was hard put to keep the provisions and other stuff in
the shallow raft. Waves ran twenty feet, maybe fifty feet
high; more than half the time he seemed to be in a trough
looking upward at Niagara Falls. It rained, and he caught
every drop he could for by now he wasn't so sure when

that ship, that ship all wrecked sailors have looked for for centuries, would arrive.

The sun beat down horribly, and one day Olson saw a long, dark shadow deep in the water beside his craft. For a moment it looked like a torpedo, but it was a shark, about ten feet long. Olson now looked at the water with particular interest. He saw another long shadow, then another and another. Godalmighty! There must be twenty of them, and presently they took to swimming up close, turning over on their sides, and leering. That was the word, leering.

Olson had a spare oar. He took it in his hands and when one of the big fish got really close, he'd wham down. Once in a while he would land one right on a shark's nose. But it didn't do any good. The water was full of long shadows. When he'd wake up in the morning, first thing he would do would be to look over the side of the raft—and they'd still be there, yawning, grinning, moving easily and noiselessly, waiting.

It gave Olson a queer feeling. One morning when he was opening a can of pemmican he cut his finger and it bled furiously. He trailed his hand in the water a moment. Instantly the water was alive with sharks, more than he had seen before, and they were frantic, threshing, splashing, leaping, until their mean snouts bumped the raft. Olson bandaged his hand and kept it out of the sea after that.

Nights he'd sleep some. Fitfully, never for long at a time. When it was dark he'd use the flashlight to signal, but after a while the battery gave out.

One day, and what day was it? he found the sharks had gone away. He made a little frame of pieces of wood. Took him the best of a day. Helped to pass the time. Next morning he started to make a net, weaving it on the frame out of bandages from the first-aid stuff. Took nearly all day for that, and the next day he rigged his net on an oar and dipped for fish. Not that he needed them but it gave him

Harley Archie Olson, Merchant Marine

something to do, something to occupy his mind, and his mind was what needed tending now.

Mostly the fish were too fast for him, but once in a while he would land one of a perfectly round species, a kind he had never seen before. It helped to pass the time.

Olson looked at his calendar one day. There were now twenty-two marks on it, but he wasn't sure it was right for he had lost faith in his counting and remembering. Was this the way it started, when a man went bughouse? He took what rope he could find and began tying knots, tying knots, and making splices, the more complicated the better.

The knots and splices helped to pass the day, but the nights were awfully long too. Memories came back to him. And dreams. Or, which was a dream and which a memory? A man just couldn't be sure. One night he was certain he heard the faraway drone of a sawmill. Yes, sir, that noise could be nothing but a sawmill, a big mill cutting long Douglas fir—you could tell by the long cuts they were making. Could his raft have rounded Cape Horn and blown up through the Pacific to the good old lumber town of Reedsport, out there in Oregon? He listened to the drone of the saws. That would be the Winchester Bay Lumber Company. He sniffed. Sure enough the aroma of fir sawdust! He heard the tugs plainly on the Umpqua River, tugs towing long booms of logs. From high on the mountain back of Reedsport came the shrill toot of a donkey engine. The boys were getting out the logs, the long stuff for the mill. And Olson could see Wade's Flats, down there below the village, and the acres upon acres of fireweed in blossom . . . It was pretty fine to sail into his old home town this way, sail into old Reedsport. Made a guy feel good. Olson sang:

"Is it pemmican, Mister Gallagher?
Absolutely, Mister Shean."

On July 7, Olson signed papers for another voyage and he hoped they'd bag a Jap or a German sub on this trip. He is now plying the seas that have been becoming grimmer places week by week, plying the seas, moving things needed by the Allies, for not even a torpedo and a month alone on a raft had any effect on the courage or patriotism of one of the boys who never get medals but possibly deserve them.

"General Wayne, his face also bloody from a head-wound, insisted on being carried along with the attack, which he never ceased to urge forward."

CITING GENERAL (*Mad*) ANTHONY WAYNE,
AT THE CAPTURE OF STONY POINT,
JULY 16, 1779.

6

O'HARE AND NINE JAPS

WHEN LIEUTENANT EDWARD HENRY O'HARE finally took his plane into the air, it looked as if the action was all over, finished. He had watched while his immediate superior, Lieutenant Commander John Thach, had shot down two big Mitsubishi bombers. He had stood by his warming Grumman Wildcat on the deck of the big carrier and watched again while Navy fighters climbed, swooped, and brought down two more Japs.

Then the skies over the American task force cleared of enemy planes. Thach and two other able pilots were away to the east, blood in their eye, harrying what was left of the first flight of bombers. O'Hare had been ordered to stand by on the carrier deck, and being a good officer that was exactly what he was doing, meanwhile feeling pretty bad about his own lack of opportunity.

It was the 20th day of February, late in that winter of 1942 when the United States felt a chill down its spine, and not the chill of winter. An American task force was in the Pacific, not far from the Jap-held Gilbert Islands. The wave of enemy bombers had been expected for hours. Now they had been met and shot down or dispersed. The skies were again clear, except for the American fighters now returning to the carrier for refueling and ammunition.

With the fighters coming in, it was now O'Hare's turn to take off, in company with one other fighter, and to cruise above the fleet to watch out for what if anything might come out of the horizon. It had been misty, with a bit of rain, but now it was clearing. O'Hare took off, climbed a bit, and circled.

Things went thus for another fifteen minutes. He felt good for his brave fellow pilots and proud of them, O'Hare did, for he is that kind of a man; but he also felt pretty bad that he had had no chance to pull his trigger on a Jap. He had never done so, and here it was late February, the war in the Pacific three months along.

O'Hare couldn't know it just then, but things were piling up for him, all a man could handle, maybe more than two or four men could handle.

He got his first sight and knowledge of them five minutes later. They were coming in from the west, where the others had come from, and he counted nine of them as he swung his Wildcat around to bear. Nine big Jap bombers.

It was a smart Jap trick, well timed too. The Japs had figured that their first flight would draw up most of the American fighters, who would shoot away their ammunition, use up their fuel, and be obliged to return to the carrier for more lead and gas. That was when the second flight would strike.

And here it was, coming out of the west, fast and at about 6,000 feet, in triple formation.

Setting his plane's nose directly in the bombers' line of flight, O'Hare looked around for his companion, the plane that had taken off when he did. He couldn't see it in the air, and looking down he glimpsed it just landing on the car-

Lieutenant Commander Edward Henry O'Hare, U.S.N.
Seated in the cockpit of his Grumman Wildcat Fighter in which
he brought down five Japanese planes while in combat. The five
Japanese flags on the fuselage indicate the number definitely
accounted for.

rier's deck—and he later learned it had gone back because its gun mechanism had jammed. It had had to return before it had even sighted a bomber.

O'Hare was only twenty-eight years old, but he was already a competent officer and flier, an Annapolis man with better than two years' flying, but no battle, experience. He knew well enough what the roaring flight of Japs was after —they were coming to soak the carrier. He knew that each of the nine Jap planes carried three machine guns and one mean cannon—thirty-six guns against him. He also knew that at that moment he and his plane were the only things in the air to stop the Japs, if they could be stopped. If he thought his chances of doing much about it were on the short end of a long shot, he didn't act that way.

Lieutenant O'Hare raced his fast little ship directly at the enemy formation, then raised her nose and climbed.

Far below, down on the decks of the carrier, of the cruisers and destroyers, men told later how they watched but did not breathe while the lone American attacked the pounding Jap formation.

When he got up to around 7,500 feet, O'Hare leveled off for an instant. The clouds had cleared, even up here. The light rain had gone. His vision was perfect.

Watching men said O'Hare came down like a falcon. He dived for the first formation with his finger on the trigger button. His guns worked beautifully as he swooped past the bombers and below, barely missing one, the squadron leader, which was now in flames. A moment later it slowly turned over on its side, then rolled over and over, and went tumbling down to become a splash, a spume of water mixed with steam.

As he turned to pull out of his dive, O'Hare caught another Jap, bursting it into flames, and he saw it go tumbling down.

That made two, if O'Hare was bothering to count.

their intense combined fire, and despite this concentrated opposition, he, by his gallant and courageous action, his extremely skillful marksmanship, making the most of every shot of his limited amount of ammunition, shot down five enemy planes and severely damaged a sixth before they reached the bomb release point.

As a result of his gallant action, one of the most daring, if not the most daring single action in the history of combat aviation, he undoubtedly saved his carrier from serious damage.

When the American Navy talks like that, you may be sure that the subject is no mere fighting man; he's one of the best fighting men on earth.

The American people like to know where their great fighting men come from. O'Hare was born in St. Louis on March 13, 1914, and attended Western Military Academy before receiving an appointment to the Naval Academy at Annapolis. He was commissioned ensign in June of 1937, and lieutenant, junior grade, in June of 1940. He became a full lieutenant (temporary) in January of 1942, a month before his great battle.

O'Hare served on the USS *New Mexico* for two years, and was then sent for aviation instruction to the Naval Air Station at Pensacola, Florida. Upon completion of his course, says the Navy's official statement, O'Hare was ". . . assigned to duty with the fighting squadrons." That proved to be exactly where he belonged.

"The bravest man I ever knew, and a perfect soldier."

CITATION OF GENERAL PHIL KEARNY,
BY GENERAL WINFIELD SCOTT, 1862.

7

OLD-FASHIONED FIGHTING MAN

IN THIS KIND OF WAR men direct the movements and mechanism of machines that tear over the ground, run swiftly over the water, or speed like birds through the skies, all intent upon killing. Never before have machines played such a part in battle. The machine that flies and fights has become so important that many believe command of the air amounts to being the command of the winning side.

It is for this reason that the ground fighters, the men armed only with rifles or sidearms, the non-machine men, have been given comparatively little attention. The place once held by the Grecian Phalanx, by the British Square, by the open-formation advance of American infantry—that is, the place of greatest importance and hence of greatest honor —has been taken in this war by the men who fly machines and fight with them. The heavy bomber, the dive-bomber, the pursuits, the fighters—these are the striking force of modern armies. Public interest, directed by press and radio, is centered on exploits in the air, and in lesser degree to the clash of navies, which are machines, and to the impact of large numbers of tanks, which are machines also.

But in this war, as in all others, men still fight on the ground. They fight grimly, filled with more personal hate perhaps than are machine fighters, and often with the fury that comes only with primeval battle, that of hand-to-hand combat. This is the kind of fighting our ancestors knew. It is accounted grubby stuff compared to the swift maneuver of machines high in the clouds, or so the press and public seem to think, and it does not get the attention in this machine-loving age that it warrants.

Many of these men with their feet on the solid earth have killed more of the enemy than have men directing the activities of intricate machinery of destruction. Now and again, one of these walking, shooting men, armed with rifle, with revolver, and perhaps a few grenades, has played more havoc with the enemy than has a tank with its three men, a bomber with its nine men, or even a destroyer and its hundred men.

Yet, and because this is so largely a war of machines, the men who run the machines will get most of the medals—but not quite all of them. On January 12, 1942, an American soldier on foot named Alexander Ramsey Ninninger fought in a fashion that the Army said displayed gallantry and intrepidity above and beyond the call to duty, which is the utmost the Army will say of any of its men.

On January 12, Second Lieutenant Ninninger had been seven months out of the Military Academy at West Point. He was twenty-four years old and an officer of the 57th Philippine Scouts stationed with his company near Abucay on the Bataan Peninsula. On that day his own company was holding a quiet sector. Elsewhere, though, Company K of the 57th was actively engaged in attempting to retake important positions which the Japs had stormed and taken.

The Jap infantry was in superior force and had dug in, and now they were sending out advance parties, sniping, getting into new fox holes. Company K was in a really bad place, one that would have to be remedied if the American lines were to hold at all.

Lieutenant Ninninger had no business with Company K, but he wanted to kill Japs, believing in his modest way that killing Japs was the way to win the war. When you killed all the Japs, the war would be over. Ninninger applied to Company K's captain for permission to move forward with the company on what Ninninger knew was to be an attempt to dislodge the enemy from his excellent and commanding position. The captain told him okay, and added that it wasn't likely to be much fun.

The serious-faced young lieutenant from Gainesville, Georgia, the state of so many great fighting men in this and other wars, at once started moving. His time was nearly out now and he used it as if he were the last American on earth fighting a world peopled wholly with Jap soldiers.

First thing Ninninger did was to crawl forward a few yards on his belly, stand up, then heave a grenade into an enemy fox hole. It blew four snipers to pieces. Carrying a regulation Army rifle with fixed bayonet, Ninninger moved ahead, this time in spite of enemy fire all around him. Here and there some of Company K's men saw the lieutenant and from them later the fighting epic of the next two hours was pieced together.

With his rifle Ninninger shot a Jap sniper through the head and out of a tree. The body fell at his feet like that of a game bird. He stepped over it and moved on. Bullets cut the leaves above him, and on both sides. A bullet struck him in the leg. He put down his rifle, got out his emergency kit, and bound the wound. Then he picked up his rifle and moved on, ahead.

Far up in a tree a yellow face looked down and one slant eye squinted along a Jap rifle. But Ninninger had been too quick. He had seen the Jap and now, with seemingly no aim, he brought down his second sniper. He moved forward again.

Ahead of him he could see a well-protected fox hole, with dirt mounds in front. Dropping to one knee the American laid down his rifle, pulled the pin of a grenade and lobbed it over. Before it struck to explode, another grenade was on the way. Both fell true, where they did an awful lot of good. The fox hole had contained six Japs. All were now dead.

Ninninger moved forward, but had to stop. Another bullet had caught him. But it wasn't enough to stop him long. He bound up the wound and walked on, still forward. By now all of Company K was moving ahead, making good progress. And by now the Japs were calling for help from their rear. Shells started coming over from enemy artillery. They blew off treetops. They blew off tree trunks, leaving weird-shaped stumps in the fraction of a second. Smoke drifted in eddies. Men suddenly grunted, then went down to stay.

Shell craters were showing up, new ones. Ninninger sometimes walked around the big holes, again he just walked into them, then up on the other side. He kept his face and his rifle in one direction, always ahead.

The Japs were moving up more machine guns to stem this advance. They rattled so a man could not hear his own rifle, and the twigs and leaves and branches of the jungle fell in a constant rain. Ninninger stopped a moment to put a new clip in his rifle. Just then the heads of two Japs showed. Ninninger shot off the top of one of the heads. He charged the other head, and when it showed a body with the head, he charged the body and ran it through with his bayonet.

Lieutenant Ninninger, men told later, was fighting what seemed to be a personal war, with the entire Jap army his antagonist. He didn't speak. He never looked back, never turned around. He did not even seem to be in a hurry. He simply plowed on ahead, killing everything in his path that moved, and seeing everything that moved as though he were a hawk high in the air.

But his time was getting close. Another bullet got him, this time through the stomach. He went down for part of the count—maybe seven, maybe eight, but not all the way. He struggled to his feet, rammed another clip into his gun, and moved again, still forward, still heading for that Jap army, that army of millions upon millions of yellow men that must be exterminated before the people of Gainesville, the people of Georgia, the people of the United States, could live in peace again. It was going to be quite a task, to kill all these vermin, but he would go on killing them as long as he had the strength and a rifle.

Ninninger, weaker now, lurched around a thick clump of bushes, and came face to face with an enemy officer and two soldiers. Dripping blood from his three wounds, the boy from Georgia was in a tough spot, but he probably didn't know it. His body was sagging, perhaps his aim wasn't so steady as it had been two hours ago, but he was still in too good shape to be taken by just three Japs, even if one of them did have a sword.

Up went Ninninger's old Army gun, and down went one Jap.

The officer and the remaining Jap soldier charged, the soldier with bayonet.

They parried for a moment, as Jap steel clanged against the American's bayonet. Then Ninninger lunged with the fury and power of a wounded buffalo. His bayonet caught the Jap right in the belly, and the man threw up his arms, then grabbed for the bayonet and slumped.

With a twist Ninninger pulled out the blade. He was on his knees, and he must have known that the count now was nine.

With a final effort he cocked his rifle, took a sort of aim and shot the Jap officer through the head just as he was coming in with upraised sword for the blow that would have beheaded the American.

When men of Company K came up, they found Ninninger dead, but with his head on his shoulders, and three wounds in his body. Around him were three dead Japs.

The Americans won back the position, and from here they managed to hold the superior numbers of Japs for many days, days that counted so heavily for the American side of the war. In the meantime, Company K's officers and men told each other the stories of what they had seen Lieutenant Ninninger do in those last few hours of his; and they followed Ninninger's trail from where he started to where he died.

It was impossible to tell how many of the enemy the lone American had accounted for. It may have been fifteen, it may have been twenty, and it could well have been twenty-five. During his charge he had wrecked half-a-dozen fox holes and machine gun positions and many of the Japs they contained. He had shot at least two snipers out of trees. And he had bayoneted or shot the last three of the enemy with whom he came in contact.

Thus died a modern fighting man who fought an old-fashioned war in the midst of planes and tanks and aircraft carriers and flame throwers.

On the recommendation of General MacArthur, Lieutenant Ninninger was awarded the Congressional Medal of Honor, the first awarded in the present war. If ever "conspicuous gallantry and intrepidity above and beyond the call to duty" was shown, then the boy from Gainesville displayed them. New heroes are being acclaimed almost daily, and they have earned the acclaim, whether the bravery was on or under the sea or high in the air. But Lieutenant

Ninninger will remain in a small and select company that bids fair to become smaller and more select as the months roll by—a common or ground hand-to-hand fighting man, and a hero to boot.

"Lieut. Hobson . . . extraordinary courage . . . beyond the call of duty . . . sinking the Merrimac *in the channel under persistent fire from the enemy fleet and fortifications on shore."*

CITING LIEUTENANT RICHMOND P. HOBSON,
SANTIAGO, CUBA, 1898.

8

UNDERSEAS FIGHTERS

THE "SEAWOLF" PREPARED to stalk her target. Her periscope had just revealed a flotilla of Jap warships and transports dead ahead, and now the slim tube disappeared beneath the ocean's surface and Lieutenant Commander Frederick B. Warder ordered his engines at half speed. Less likely to be detected that way. Commander Warder couldn't tell, from the fleeting glance in the mirrors, just how many enemy vessels made up the convoy, nor of what class. He would have to get closer, then do his choosing.

The water was shallow here off Christmas Island near the coast of Java; and narrow, too. Not much room for maneuvering a sub; and less room for the maneuvers of a sub's intended prey. There wasn't much room for diving, either, to escape the shaking depth charges that were sure to follow the first torpedo. But the Japs were landing in force on Java, and just ahead there looked to be a mighty fine chance to reduce that force materially. That is, if the *Seawolf* were not detected too soon, if she behaved well in these swift, tricky currents, and if the torpedoes did not pick this particular day to act in an erratic manner, as torpedoes sometimes do.

Commander Warder was sure of his craft. He had watched her being built at Portsmouth, New Hampshire, back in 1937. He had been in charge of fitting her out and he had assumed command when she was commissioned on the first day of December 1939. He knew every plate and rivet in her long slippery body. And Commander Warder knew his torpedoes. He had been learning about them ever since he was graduated from the Naval Academy in 1925, when he was a stripling of twenty-one. He was familiar with each of the 1,300 parts contained in every tin fish aboard the *Seawolf*.

There are not many machines more complicated than a modern American torpedo. Its nose, which is the business end, is called a war head. This is a light casting of bronze containing some five hundred pounds of TNT and a small detonating charge. The war head isn't meant to penetrate anything and it doesn't. It may not even dent the hull of a ship. But the impact of the war head on the hull sets off the TNT which uses the water as a battering ram; the rush of water is what smashes in the ship's side and sinks her.

The propelling part of a torpedo is just behind the war head. This is the air flask, a chamber of compressed air. As the big missile is launched from the sub, a jet of compressed air shoots into another chamber. Another jet forces fuel alcohol into the same chamber. The combination of air and alcohol forms an inflammable spray. Meanwhile still another jet of air works an igniter which explodes a cartridge to ignite the spray. Meanwhile, too, one more jet of air starts a self-operating water pot. The pot starts spraying water on the flame to produce steam.

All this sounds mighty complicated and it is, and it gets things going. The entire operation described takes but a moment, and thus a mixture of steam, gas, and compressed air has the torpedo's turbines rolling immediately and developing 400 horsepower to the propellers.

But the missile's course must be directed. So, at the same time the propelling machinery gets under way, a jet of air starts a gyroscope spinning. Should cross currents or heavy seas take the fish off its course, which has been set on its steering instruments, the gyroscope will operate vertical rudders to steer it back. The gyro can also be set to produce what is called an angle shot—that is, the torpedo changes its course in mid-voyage.

Today, however, there would be no call for an angle shot. The prey was somewhere ahead and in open water, open except for a protecting screen of destroyers. Commander Warder took another look through the periscope. The sub was moving forward slowly and just beneath the surface. The mirrors now gave a fine view: Dead ahead was the broad hull of a big transport. Slightly aft of her was a Jap destroyer, and another destroyer just beyond. Commander Warder estimated their speed and range, then gave his orders.

The *Seawolf's* torps men had been at their stations and waiting. Not one of them could see the target and they didn't need to. One after the other Commander Warder called the range, the speed, and the course; and the torps men began setting the mechanical brain of their lethal fish. They did this by twisting dials, moving gadgets, pulling little levers.

"Ready, sir," came through the phone to the commander.

"Hold her steady," Commander Warder told his helmsman, then: "Fire one."

The outer door which had kept the Pacific ocean out of the torpedo's tube now opened. There came a loud whissshh of compressed air. The submarine jarred slightly as the fish leaped clear and started to buck erratically until its mechanism got to working. Now it sped in a straight, grim line that was marked on the surface, if the Japs ever saw it, by a continuing row of bubbles.

Commander Warder ordered his helmsman on a new

course, and meanwhile kept his eye at the periscope's mirrors. He couldn't follow the wake of his fish, but in about ten seconds he saw a vast plume of water rise high over the transport's starboard side. It was a perfect hit, amidships. Another two seconds and the *Seawolf* herself shivered and shook from the explosion of the distant torpedo.

The *Seawolf's* skipper kept his eye to the mirror for another few moments. He saw the big transport heave, up, up, up, in a big roll, then list, then roll right over and start to sink.

That was fine, swell, good!

The *Seawolf's* skipper, his eye still at the mirror, also saw something else. He saw two Jap destroyers, black smoke rolling from their stacks, come dashing toward him. The *Seawolf* took in her periscope and dived, changing her course as she went deeper into the Java Sea.

Now began a period of hell for the crew of the sub. You haven't got to be filled with phobias about space to understand the feeling a man can have when he is shut up in a steel tube, under the sea, and awaiting an attack from outside. It is, it must be a feeling inherent in the human mind— a feeling of being trapped, of being blind and deaf, of helplessness in the face of things beyond control.

Commander Warder pushed the button for general alarm. The siren shrieked mournfully through the diving sub and the crew moved to quarters—for a depth charge attack. It came instantly—a jarring crash that jolted the *Seawolf* off her course as if an earthquake had hit it, a crash that shivered the timbers of every one of the *Seawolf's* crew.

A minute later came another crash, more violent than the first. Men were thrown off their pins and fell flat, and in the crowded quarters officers and men grabbed and clung to whatever would hold to keep them from being battered senseless on the submarine's hull and against the compartments and bulkheads.

Lieutenant Commander Frederick B. Warder, U.S.N.

They could hear the destroyers rushing back and forth overhead, could hear them as they circled and came back to dump another charge. The *Seawolf* rocked and rocked again. The water rushed through her superstructure with a weird swishing noise. That kind of noise, as Commander Warder knew, meant that the depth bombs had been mighty close— almost too close. But the *Seawolf's* sturdy sides and seams held. Not a drop of water came through.

Changing his course often, running as deep as he dared in these waters, Warder now shut off the engines to wait until the first flurry on the surface had passed. After a time the depth charges became fewer, then ceased.

Warily, the submarine's engines started again, very slowly, and he went up for a look. Two Jap destroyers were all that the periscope showed, and that was enough. "Stand by for Number Two," Warder ordered, then called figures for the torps men.

"Ready on Number Two, sir."

Warder had picked the nearer of the destroyers. It looked like a good clean target.

"Fire Number Two." Again came the whish and the jar as the missile started on its way. It struck fair, a beauty of a shot on the port bow. Warder kept his periscope up until he saw the warship start sinking.

Again the sub's crew went through the jarring uncertainty of depth bombing, but this time a bombing from one and not two destroyers. They watched the *Seawolf's* seams for signs of the first telltale drop of water. No leaks showed and the undersea raider left the scene of action without a scar or a sprung seam.

The *Seawolf* didn't go far that night, only far enough to rest in comparative safety. Next day she came back to her hunting grounds. It was one of the busiest and best days the *Seawolf* would ever know. Warder and his sharpshooting crew put their first two torpedoes into the belly of a Jap light cruiser. She sank then and there.

The raider's next fish struck a second light cruiser.

God! but this was a great day.

And the next torpedo whammed into a third light cruiser, setting her to listing immediately.

Warder never knew for sure whether or not the two damaged ships sank, but he left them in grave trouble; and he was certain of sinking one light cruiser anyway. It was a good day's work.

The prowl through the South Seas of the *Seawolf* was becoming one of the most enemy-destroying forays in American naval history. Working alone, with a highly capable crew and his three officers, Lieutenant William N. Deragon, Lieutenant Richard Holden, and Ensign James Mercer, Commander Warder, the seagoing pride of Grafton, West Virginia, was demonstrating submarine warfare at its most offensive.

During the period from February into April of 1942, the lone undersea raider took an enormous toll of Jap warships and other vessels. On routine patrol off Bali she attacked and damaged a large transport. Later in the month she sank the enemy destroyer and transport already mentioned. After her opening action off Christmas Island the *Seawolf* continued operations in the vicinity, hitting at least four light cruisers.

During the early morning of March 31, the raider struck a Jap light cruiser with one and possibly two torpedoes. On the next night she hit a cruiser twice and sank her, and on the same day damaged a light cruiser. After two and a half months of constant patrol, happily punctuated with destruction, the *Seawolf* returned to her base unscarred and with every man at his post. Perhaps it was a record cruise of an American sub. In any case, it was good enough. The Navy

gave Commander Warder its Cross on the recommendation
of tough and appreciative Vice Admiral Herbert F. Leary.

A different sort of cruise, and probably just as interesting
as that of the *Seawolf*, was that of the submarine commanded
by Lieutenant Frank W. Fenno, formerly of tiny Westmin-
ster, Massachusetts. One night early in February, 1942,
Commander Fenno got his orders: "Proceed to Fort Mills
on Corregidor Island where the commandant will issue new
orders of a very special nature."

Commander Fenno's sub was loaded with anti-aircraft ammunition. He arrived at Fort Mills under cover of darkness
on the night of February 3, and unloaded. Then he began
taking aboard a strange cargo for a sub. It was nothing but
gold and silver.

This was the treasure from twelve banks in Manila. It
had been taken out of the city under direction of Woodbury
Willoughby, financial advisor to Francis B. Sayre, Philippine High Commissioner, and moved to a large vault in the
depths of Corregidor.

Gold and silver coin from the Philippine Treasury was in
the hoard, and gold in bars from mining companies. Private
citizens, during the days Manila was falling, turned over
their securities and currency. At the banks, all but the safe-
deposit boxes were emptied. There was not time for them.
Jap planes were bombing the city and bombing Corregidor
and bombing every ship that moved in Manila Bay. An office
building of the Philippine Treasury was blown to bits by a
direct hit just as Willoughby's men took out the last box of
valuables.

Using every boat they could lay hands on—tugs, fishing
smacks, pleasure craft—Willoughby's men took the stuff
across the Bay while Manila's sirens screamed and Jap
planes dumped bombs all around the small bobbing craft.

The problem of currency was considered. Here were bale upon bale of bank notes. Willoughby's men, working in three shifts, tore open the bundles, recorded the serial numbers on the notes and the owners, then burned the notes.

Transfer of the tons of specie from a city under heavy bombardment across open water and to a fort also under bombardment was a task calling for speed and courage and organization. All three factors were present.

Well, Lieutenant Commander Fenno had his orders and now he prepared to stow away millions of dollars in the narrow confines of his submarine. It required two nights to do the job, for work ceased at dawn, when the sub retired to deep water to wait upon darkness again.

A motley crew helped to load the treasure those two hectic nights. Army and Navy officers, members of Commissioner Sayre's staff, and Filipino stevedores, all lugged heavy boxes from the vault to the dock and stowed them where Commander Fenno ordered. Even a vice-president got slivers in his hands. He was Sergio Osmena, second-in-command of the Philippine Commonwealth. And General Valdes of the Philippine Army also lent a hand.

The loading, except for several bales of securities which were not ready, was finished just before dawn on February 4, and the sub put away from shore and sank slowly out of sight. Commander Fenno had been ordered to meet a Navy surface vessel at a certain hour that night. He now steered a course out into Manila Bay, then submerged to the bottom.

It was one of the longest days Commander Fenno and his crew ever knew, for only part of the tired men could go to their bunks. Someone must stand watch. There they were, a sub with the wealth of Manila, with much of the portable wealth of the Philippine Islands in her hull, lying deep and quiet beneath the waters of Manila Bay. The minutes were hours that day. But no plane had sighted the sub's movements, and no depth charges shook the cat naps of her crew.

Darkness finally came. This was going to be a ticklish business, this meeting a surface vessel in the harbor to transfer the bales of securities that had not been ready.

The Navy vessel stood out from Corregidor under a cloudy sky. The sub surfaced with a mild noise only a few yards away. The range and timing had been perfect, and it had better be, for a slip tonight, the mere flash of a light, the sound of a box, of a port, anything might rouse the alert Japs on shore and in the sky. Shore searchlights played arcs across the water. Unseen planes droned past overhead. It was a time and place of high tension.

Commander Fenno brought his sub alongside. The Bay was fairly smooth.

Only twenty minutes were required to transfer the securities in the night that got darker as it progressed. When all had been stowed below, Commander Fenno, standing on the sub's conning tower, asked the skipper of the surface craft a final question that ought to be historic:

"Are there any passengers?" enquired Commander Fenno softly.

There being none, he closed the tower and gave the order to submerge. Men on board the Navy vessel saw the sub sink noiselessly out of sight, and they wondered how she would do on the long and hazardous voyage ahead of her.

She did all right. Commander Fenno brought her into Pearl Harbor days later and the treasure was put aboard a Navy cruiser for San Francisco, where it arrived safely.

To Commander Frank W. Fenno, the man who wanted some passengers to go with his freight, went the Navy Cross, and to each of his officers and men the Navy's Silver Star. The sub's officers represented a good piece of American geography. They were Lieutenants: Albert Hobbs Clark, Washington, D. C.; Frederick Arthur Gunn, Kansas City, Kansas; Frederick J. Harlfinger, 2nd, East Nassau, New York; Harry Eades Woodworth, Spokane, Washington; and Ensigns: Raymond L. Pitts, Oxnard, California; and George H. Schottler, Baltimore, Maryland.

All of the citations to both officers and men were "For extraordinary heroism."

And the Army, taking cognizance of the voyage, awarded its Distinguished Service Cross to Commander Fenno.

Another submarine commander had an unusual experience —a duel with an enemy submarine. The American was Lieutenant Commander Elton W. Grenfell of Radburn Place, New Jersey.

Commander Grenfell's undersea craft, operating in the South Pacific, had just sunk an enemy vessel and was homeward bound, running on the surface. His radio brought a message: "Enemy submarine is operating in your general vicinity."

The Pacific Ocean is large country and the likelihood of running across the enemy sub, even if searching for it, would be rather remote. But Grenfell would be ready if it happened. He submerged to periscope depth, ran up the mirrored tube, and took a squint into his end of the rigging.

Now, naval officers do not swear; they merely emit ejaculations. And what Commander Grenfell saw in the mirror caused him to emit his best ejaculation and it wasn't: "Goody!" The mirror showed a Jap submarine, proceeding on the surface and with her lookouts obviously unaware of the American's presence.

Grenfell shouted his orders. In two minutes his men called out: "Ready, sir." He pressed the button, and a torpedo whished away. It missed. He let go another. It struck home. He let go a third. It struck home. The Jap disappeared.

Commander Grenfell believed it sank, but because the Navy is extremely careful about verification of submarine sinkings, he called it "severely damaged" instead of "sunk." And the Navy hung its Cross on its dueling lieutenant commander.

A Navy Cross went to several other gallant and destructive skippers of American submarines. One each to Lieutenant Commander Willis A. Lent, West Roxbury, Massachusetts, whose sub was credited with sinking a total of 27,000 tons of enemy shipping; to Lieutenant Commander John L. DeTar, Philadelphia, who sank a Jap freighter, damaged and "probably sank" one Jap destroyer, and damaged two other enemy ships of undetermined class; to Lieutenant Commander David C. White, San Diego, California; to Lieutenant Commander Lewis S. Parks, Wilmington, Delaware, and to Lieutenant Commander Stanley P. Moseley, Fort Worth, Texas.

"Remember the Alamo!"

BATTLE CRY OF THE TEXANS
AT SAN JACINTO, 1836.

9

RAID ON TOKYO

As THE FIRST of three flights of American bombers approached the mainland, Lieutenant Colonel James H. Doolittle, commander of the squadron, and his men heard a Japanese radio announcer at work on a pretty fine propaganda broadcast in English.

"Life in Japan go happily on as before," cooed the voice, dripping sugar in the best American commercial radio manner. "The Japanese people, they enjoy beautiful scenery in wartime, as always. No enemy can approach our delicious flowery kingdom. We are too powerful. No one dare to . . ."

The voice dripped on, and Doolittle's men smiled, then let go belly laughs as a listening American sergeant issued a juicy Bronx cheer over the leading plane's interphone.

The American planes were medium bombers, North American B-25's. The time was midmorning. The date, April 18, 1942, thus putting demands on some future poet who will recall Longfellow's lines on Paul Revere.

This first raid by an enemy on Japan's mainland in modern Japan's history had been planned for a long time. Every one of the seventy-nine officers and men with Doolittle was a volunteer. The preparations had consumed weeks, for you don't, in spite of general public opinion, just say "We'll raid Japan" or any other place and do it right then. At least not the kind of a raid this one was to be. Detailed maps had been studied, checked and marked, especially in reference to the sites of aircraft factories, tank factories, shipyards, munitions plants of all sorts. Each plane was given specific targets.

Distances between points to be bombed were carefully calculated, and flying time reckoned to the second. The loads of gasoline and bombs, both high explosive and incendiary, were figured.

The plans even took into consideration the chance, or rather the seeming inevitability, that one or more American planes would fall into the hands of the enemy; all of the Norden bombsights were removed from the planes, and in their places went an improvised gadget that cost twenty cents each to install. This dime-store sight, still very much of a military secret, had been designed by Captain Charles H. Greening of Tacoma, Washington, the armament officer of the raiding party. This was to be its first test in action against an enemy.

The voice of the happy Jap announcer still came into the advancing planes: ". . . and Japanese people, unlike other nation at war, have much good fish and rice on their table. We are . . ."

The first flight now sighted the mainland, rising out of a sea that was bright in the morning sun. The planes slanted down, down almost to the ocean, and came in fast, just above the tops of trees along the shore. On the beach some kids were at play. They stopped to look up in amazement at planes coming over them so low. And as the flight whizzed past, two of the youngsters picked up stones and threw them as hard as they could at the raiders.

Inland went the flight, the other two squadrons coming on at just the right intervals.

No fighters rose to greet the invaders. Japan had never been raided within the memory of the oldest citizen, and it expected no raiders now. Still, the Americans wondered if Jap military listening posts could fail to hear the pounding engines of more than a dozen bombers.

The Americans looked down on Japan in April, a checkerboard of different shades of green in its rural districts. The rice paddies were dry at this season, dry but not loafing, for now they were growing grain and *daikon* radishes, the universal root vegetable. Here and there a cart plodded along a country road.

On went the raiders, hugging close to the treetops, roaring over the heads of Jap farmers working on the endless terraces. It was odd the way different farmers reacted to the invading armada. Some never looked up from their work, thinking no doubt that these were planes of the Son of Heaven on patrol to keep the awful foreign devils from their shores. But other farmers looked up, then ran for the nearest cover.

The Jap announcer was still hard at work: ". . . and our fine artists today, as always, are painting lovely picture of tree and flowers and mountain, the same as have always been done since . . ."

The leading plane climbed to 1,500 feet, then leveled off, the others following in perfect formation. It was like a drill of the ablest pilots and crews and planes to be found. Precision.

The country below began to change rapidly. Farms gave way to small suburbs. The smoke of great cities, and industries, appeared not far ahead. Still holding 1,500 feet the planes tore along at 300 miles an hour. Then orders inside the ships were given.

"Prepare to bomb."

Mechanics adjusted the bomb-bay door gear. Bombardiers looked to their twenty-cent sights. Now the first flight was almost over a vast, busy, smoking plant, acres upon acres of it.

"Let her go," said Lieutenant Colonel Doolittle.

The bomb-bay doors banged open, and a second later tons of heavy powerful destruction were on their way downward, whistling mean as they went and ending in mighty roars. They had hit the plant on the chin, on the nose, on the solar plexus. In another moment this aircraft factory was in red and yellow flames, with rubble all around.

The first flight now slanted down again and left the city, hedgehopping the parklike trees. Behind them the second flight was performing as prearranged. Each plane had a specific target—and found it. The second flight plastered a busy railroad junction. The second flight also saw plant fire brigades turning out to fight a fire which had come without a moment's warning.

The third flight came on to find both factory and railroad yards in flames and confusion. They dropped their tons of stuff on a portion of a navy yard, where big ships were under construction.

Still the happy Jap announcer hadn't heard the news. He cooed on: ". . . our young peoples enjoy their sports. Today there is a nice baseball game at . . ."

The sergeant in Doolittle's plane now made an observation through the interphone. "I wonder," he said, "if we can't do anything to stop that guy's bedtime stories?"

The Jap air force, at least, had been apprised of the news. Four fighters came up to attack the plane piloted by Captain Greening. Greening put his plane as low to the ground as he dared, once even flying under some power lines, hoping the fighters would crash in the heavy wires. They didn't. They kept right on Greening's tail, shooting.

Greening's gunners were shooting too. And suddenly with

one big burst of fire, they shot down two of the pursuing Japs. The Americans put on all the power they had and left the other two Japs behind. Now Greening rose for his bombing run.

The objective was a gasoline refinery and some huge oil storage tanks. It had all been well camouflaged, but the raiders knew exactly where it was. At 1,500 feet the bombs were let go, and before the plane could get away a terrific explosion shook it like a rat, throwing Greening and his co-pilot, in spite of their belts, right up out of their seats to bang their heads hard on the roof of the cockpit. As the plane roared on its way the rear gunner reported immense sheets of flames and smoke spreading out from the refinery.

By now even the joyous Jap radio man had learned something was wrong. He went off the air in the middle of a joyous sentence—just like that; and a moment later a voice began in Japanese. It was an excited voice, almost incoherent even to the two American raiders who understood the language. It told of horrible destruction, of bombs raining down all over Japan, of hospitals and schools being blown to smithereens, of whole cities in flames from incendiaries. "Thousands of planes," he chattered.

It was fun to raid a land and to hear a voice turn from English to Japanese and from smugness to panic, all in an instant.

The planes pounded on.

It was noon as the flights raced over Tokyo, right down close to the trees again, only a few yards above the houses. When the first flight zipped over the municipal ball park, the bleachers and grandstand were filled, a man was at bat, all players in place. The raiders saw thousands of faces turned upward in wonder at planes that flew so near that their noise drowned the umpire's voice. The park and all in it, in fact, seemed to be frozen—just like the stopping of a moving picture in mid-action. The raiders were so close they marked the expression of amazement, not yet of fear, that obviously prevailed on the sea of upturned faces.

The first flight passed on. They saw the Imperial Palace below them, as fair a target as a man could wish; but the orders were: No bombs on the Palace.

The second flight came over the ball park, and the Americans saw men rising from their seats, while the players were just starting to run for whatever it is Jap baseball teams call the dugouts. Panic wasn't on yet. It was just beginning.

The second flight roared on to strew incendiary bombs the full length of an aircraft factory.

The third flight came over the ball park, and this time panic was in full swing. Men were tumbling over other men, rolling down aisles, struggling, striking out with both arms, screaming, jumping. So were women. The players were running like the wind for cover. One deck of bleachers gave way with a crash, letting hundreds of persons fall into a pile of squirming arms and legs and bodies.

It was the damnedest ending to a ball game Tokyo had ever seen. The third flight of Americans could positively report that the game was over. They went on to strike a dockyard, and to break off the arms of a gigantic crane as though it had been of bread crust.

In Tokyo's teeming streets fire engines were screaming. Trucks of soldiers were pounding through the squares. The anti-aircraft had at last got under way and were firing wildly in every direction, causing more damage to civilians than to the raiders.

Radio Tokyo was in full panic too, its excited voice fairly chattering that thousands of enemy planes were attacking the Empire from all sides, doing terrible destruction.

Radio Tokyo was wrong about the number of planes, but quite correct about the damage.

All of the big coastal cities felt the raiders' weight— Yokosuka, Nagoya, Osaka, Kobe, Yokohama, Tokyo itself.

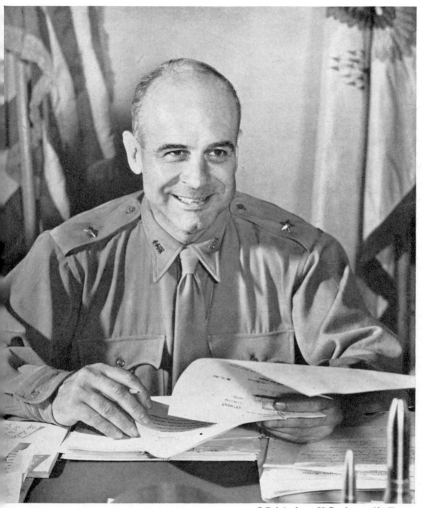

Brigadier General James H. Doolittle

The raid took in an area roughly forty miles long and from five to twenty miles wide, the area in which virtually all of Japan's industries, either of peace or of war, are located.

The Americans hit a new battleship fair, in the navy yard south of Tokyo. At Nagoya they bombed and set fire to the big aircraft factory. They chewed up a large tank farm. Set fire to a refinery. Damaged a steel works, and a number of railroad junctions and yards. They blew up ammunition dumps and factories. As the raiders, their mission ended, turned to fly home to their base, they could see columns of smoke rising thousands of feet from many points. The smoke was visible from as far as thirty miles at sea.

Colonel Doolittle reported that the incendiary bombs used had proved excellent. He saw the patterns of small sheets of flame left from the flight over Tokyo, and the following flight of planes said the entire section was burning briskly. The Jap radio boys began asking the people to pray at their shrines for rain, and it was not until two days later that Radio Tokyo reported the fires to be under control.

NOT ONE AMERICAN plane was lost. American casualties, if any, were not reported. One of the raiding planes kept on westward, to land in Siberia where its crew of five were interned by the Russians.

The Jap radio announcers, recovering from their panic and returning to their normal deception, first reported that no less than nine American bombers had been shot down. They dropped this number to two, then to one. In its final phase, this report had one of the raiders brought down "on a remote mountain," just the sort of place from which curious Jap citizens could hardly expect any survivors for display purposes.

To keep the gag alive, Japs later exhibited parts of two wrecked planes, with American insignia clearly visible. The insignia was so visible, in fact, there is good reason to believe it was a hurried home-made job. Doolittle had stated, very carefully, that "we came out without leaving a single plane behind on the Japanese mainland." The wrecked planes the Japs dug up were phonies.

Colonel Doolittle returned to the United States to receive the highest award any American fighting man can have. At the White House the President pinned the Congressional Medal of Honor on him, and he was advanced to the rank of brigadier general.

General Doolittle had had a colorful career before the Tokyo raid. In 1942 he was forty-five years old, a short, spare, balding man, who moves quickly and speaks bluntly. He expresses himself forcibly but in a cool voice. When asked if Japan was a beautiful country viewed from the air, he replied: "I loathe Japan and all it stands for so deeply that I couldn't see anything beautiful about it. I thoroughly enjoyed bombing it."

Probably General Doolittle had never cared much for Japs anyway, having been born in California. As a boy he was taken by his parents to Nome, Alaska, then in its hectic gold rush period. He completed his schooling in Los Angeles, served in the Signal Corps as a private in 1917, and was later commissioned a second lieutenant in the reserves.

He began a career of flying that brought him practically all of the important aviation trophies. He is credited with the first blind flight, in 1929. He flew nonstop from Florida to California, quite a feat in 1922. He broke the world speed record for land planes in 1932. He once, with two broken ankles in plaster casts, demonstrated a plane. On the day of Pearl Harbor he told friends at Los Angeles Municipal Airport: "I'm going to get into this thing with both feet. I'm going to Tokyo with a load of bombs."

If General Doolittle proposed such a raid to the War Department, it was a secret well kept. Not even a New York or Washington newspaper or radio commentator learned of it until the great, black headlines were on the streets. Later, when a score or more of cities, in which funds had been raised as gifts to the man who should first drop a bomb on Tokyo, attempted to find out who that man was, General Doolittle replied it was impossible to say, that several planes had begun bombing at the same moment.

Each of the seventy-nine volunteers with Doolittle in the raid was awarded a Distinguished Service Cross. These are the men whose daring feat and spectacular success thrilled every American who could read, and even those who couldn't read but could hear:

Major J. A. Hilger; Captains: C. R. Greening, D. M. Jones, E. J. York; Lieutenants: T. Hoover, W. M. Bower, R. M. Gray, E. W. Holstrom, T. Lawson, H. F. Watson, R. O. Joyce, E. E. McElroy, D. G. Smith, W. D. Farrow, D. E. Hallmark, R. E. Cole, W. N. Fitzhugh, J. E. Manch, C. J. Ozuk, L. N. Youngblood, R. R. Wilder, R. Meder, Dean Davenport, R. G. Emmens, J. M. Parker, Jr., J. R. Stork, K. E. Reddy, T. H. Blanton, R. A. Knobloch, J. A. Sims, G. P. Williams, R. L. Hite, H. A. Potter, C. N. Wildner, H. C. McCool, E. F. McGurl, C. J. Neilson, R. S. Clever, N. A. Herndon, T. C. Griffin, H. E. Crouch, F. A. Kappalcr, W. R. Pound, C. J. Campbell, J. H. Macia, H. A. Sessler, G. Barr, R. E. Miller, T. R. White, D. N. Truelove, Charles L. McClure;

Technical Sergeants: E. V. Scott, W. J. Bither; Staff Sergeants: P. J. Leonard, F. A. Braemer, Theodore H. Laban, E. W. Horton, Jr., W. L. Birch, O. A. Duquetts, J. Eierman, E. B. Bain;

Sergeants: D. V. Radney, A. E. Jones, R. J. Stephens, William J. Dieter, B. W. Pohl, Wayne M. Bissell, G. E. Larkin, Jr., M. J. Gardner, A. R. Williams, R. C. Bourgeois, E. J. Saylor, J. W. Manske, H. A. Spatz;

Corporals: B. Jordon, Donald E. Fitzmaurice, L. D. Faktor, Jacob Deshazer, David J. Thatcher.

A casual study of that list would indicate that all of the races and nationalities which make the United States are represented.

The raid itself was to Americans the best as well as the most sensational news that had come out of the war. Reflective persons were as thrilled as those of lower boiling points when the press and radio reported that Japan not only could be bombed but had been. Reflective persons also pondered the official reports of the raid. These reports indicated the Japs to have been taken wholly by surprise, and that the surprise quickly turned to something close to hysteria.

Hysteria is no doubt possible in any race, but it was not a failing accredited to the Japs by people who have lived among them. The Japs have been thought by most occidentals as almost as calm, as imperturbable, as the Chinese, especially when under stress. But panic certainly took place at that noonday baseball game in Tokyo, and in the streets of many cities that day.

Perhaps, underneath the usual Jap surface calm, there is a repressed volatility. If so, it must also be present under the surface of the dead-pan of the Jap military forces. Many American Army officers believe so and are looking forward to the day when even greater and more devastating *surprise* attacks can be made on Japan's cities and military establishments.

In any case, the fact that the surprised Japs did go into a panic should not be accepted too smugly, at least not by a nation which contains a sizable segment of people who not long ago staged a panic of their own in fear of an attack by men from the planet Mars.

It was a great 18th of April, anyway, one to be chiseled into the granite of monuments. The Doolittle Raid, as it is already commonly known in the United States, will surely go down in our history as one of its finest set pieces—a daringly conceived and brilliantly executed coup that dims the just as daring but less successful exploits of General Jubal Early and Lieutenant Richmond P. Hobson, two heroes of other American wars.

"I propose to fight it out on this line if it takes all summer."

GENERAL U. S. GRANT, 1864.

10

THE SAGA OF THE PIGEON

THE UNITED STATES NAVY gave Lieutenant Commander Dick Hawes a second Navy Cross, but it was evident they did not expect to see him again. On May 13, 1942, an official Navy communiqué referred to Hawes as follows:

Somewhere in the void which swallows up warriors who are out-numbered and overwhelmed are Lieutenant Commander Richard E. Hawes and his men, presumably prisoners of war . . .

What the Navy meant, of course, was that Hawes and his men *either* were prisoners of war, or dead. They had the best of reasons for thinking so.

But Dick Hawes and his tough crew were not swallowed up in any void. Two days later they were reported safe, and, by late May, Hawes was in Washington, preparing for a brief furlough at his home in Thomson, Georgia.

The Jap's futile attempt to put Commander Hawes into the void began on December 10, in Manila Bay, when air raid alarms sounded and out of the north came a swarm of Jap planes. Hawes was in command of the little mine-sweeper

Pigeon, 187 feet of stout timbers but hardly built to with-
stand attack by bombs or machine gun fire.

At the moment of alarm the *Pigeon* was moored at Cavite
Navy Yard, in the midst of a five-ship nest which included
two submarines and two other mine-sweepers. The *Pigeon*
was alert, with steam up and engines warm, but she wasn't
quite all there; her regular steering gear was undergoing
repair in the Yard.

Before the wailing alarms had ceased, both the *Pigeon* and
the *Quail,* another mine-sweeper, had cleared dock and were
maneuvering in the Bay to avoid bombs. Bombs were coming
down. One string fell some 200 yards to port, and the
Pigeon shook and rocked. The next string was close, only
200 feet astern, and the *Pigeon* was lifted bodily from the
water by the shock. Waves foamed over her low decks. But
she was still in one piece, and floating.

Things ashore were getting very bad. "The Navy Yard
was seen to be in flames," Commander Hawes later reported
in laconic Georgia style, "so the *Pigeon* returned to render
assistance."

The Yard at Cavite was indeed in flames. Hell was dropping on it every second. Bombs were coming down from a
score, some said twoscore, of Jap planes. Explosions were
upending whole buildings, blowing them into the harbor.
As the *Pigeon* approached, still under heavy bombing and
machine gun fire, it looked to be entering a chaos of complete destruction. But she held her course, going directly
to a submarine that had been damaged and could not move
from its place at dock. Men of the *Pigeon,* aided by the
trapped sub's crew, ran a line between the ships. "Give her
all she's got," Hawes told his engineer.

Meantime the Cavite dock was being blown to pieces. It
had been lined with American torpedoes and bombs, rows and
rows, piles and piles of them, and the Jap hits were setting
them off. Flaming hunks of steel and other debris were being

blown far across the *Pigeon's* bows. The noise was terrific; orders could be given by arm signals only. Splashes of bombs from the air were still rocking the sweeper, and some were fearfully close.

With her engines going for all they were worth, the *Pigeon* started towing the sub, and did get it clear of the dock. Then the sub rammed a mud bank straight out from dock— rammed it hard. This happened to be the exact moment a tremendous bomb came down out of the worried skies to land fair on top of a huge oil tank on the dock. It went up with a roar that was heard for miles above the sounds of battle, and it sent a horizontal sheet of fire rolling out over the water.

"It looked," says Commander Hawes's official report, "as though the submarine and *Pigeon* both were in a perilous position." Commander Hawes is not one to exaggerate.

On rolled the flames, coming nearer to the rammed sub and its would-be rescuer. The heat blistered the sides of the sweeper and the paint began to run like new sap. The place around there was as hot as men can stand and live. And it must have looked as if things were all over.

But then, as Hawes recalls it, the fire receded. "I could see that stuff rolling over the water, blazing right high and hot," he says. "I was scared. Godalmighty scared. What scared me was I couldn't do anything about it. There we were, the sub and us, with the oil a-rolling and blazing. Nobody's ever scared if he can do something about what's coming, but here was that mess of oil. We couldn't stop it. We couldn't leave the sub. We'd all have been burned to death in another five minutes, but the wind, or tide, or something, stopped the flow toward us, and it saved our hides, every one."

Working like mad, with part of the *Pigeon's* small crew steering by the tiller ropes, the sweeper got the undersea boat off the mudbank and into the harbor channel.

All of the *Pigeon's* men weren't steering. Her machine gun crews had been at their posts, and now as three two-motored Japs came down to strafe the *Pigeon* and other ships, they turned loose at close range. They hit all three of the Japs, and at least two of the planes were seen to change their course very suddenly, as if hit hard, then to fly away over the southern end of Corregidor. (It was learned later that one of the Japs exploded and fell between Monja Island Light and Corregidor, and the two others crashed just beyond. "The *Pigeon* was a falcon at heart," Hawes likes to say.)

With the sub's crew safe and her engines running again, the *Pigeon* turned to other work, of which there was plenty to do. Seeing a lighter afire, the *Pigeon* put out two men in a surf boat to haul the lighter away from the dock and moor her to a buoy.

The bombing kept on. During it, the *Pigeon's* pet monkey, a baby named Mike, had a terrible time. It would run first to one of the crew, then another, chattering its dismal fright, appealing for protection; and whenever a bomb struck fairly close, Mike's tiny hands would go up to protect his head, and he would moan pitifully.

After a while the bombing ceased, and the hard, dirty work, the kind you don't read about in most accounts of battles, began. The *Pigeon* moved ships out of the Navy Yard, and anchored them in the Bay. It installed anti-aircraft guns on a sister ship, the *Tanager*. It took aboard ammunition and distributed it to other ships. It transported deckload after deckload of torpedoes, equipment, and supplies. It took time out to salvage seventeen torpedoes. One night, when helping to repair a damaged submarine, Commander Hawes, an old diver from way down, got into a suit and went below to help with the work.

Until the fall of Corregidor, the *Pigeon* and its crew had

Lieutenant Commander Richard E. Hawes, U.S.N.

little time to worry, other than for the lack of chewing tobacco which, Commander Hawes says, "caused no little suffering."

During the final Jap attack on Corregidor, the *Pigeon* was again under intense enemy fire and was so badly damaged she started to sink—and sunk. But her crew managed to escape at the last moment to another vessel, although they left so fast they lost all of their belongings.

Commander Hawes was particularly happy about one personal item he was obliged to leave on his ship. It was a pair of new shoes. "Most terrible pair of shoes you ever saw," he says. He had worn them once, and they put his feet in such shape that he trod his deck barefoot for a week afterward. "I hope," he says, "that the Jap who got those shoes tries to wear them. He'll sure know the tortures of hell."

But Hawes is sorry about another thing he had to leave on the *Pigeon*. That was his Civilian Conservation Corps medal, given to him not for bravery but for "good work" as commander of a CCC camp in Connecticut.

"I thought more of that medal than anything I had," he said. "Hope they can fix me up with another one like it. The CCC was the greatest thing this or any other government ever did for boys and young men. It helped no end of them. It made thousands of boys better men, for civilian life or as sailors and soldiers. It teaches them how to take care of themselves."

Lieutenant Commander Richard E. Hawes is one of the finest examples to be found of the man who has come up through the ranks. Born in small Thomson, Georgia, in 1897, he attended college and law school, enlisted in the Navy in 1917, was promoted to ensign (temporary), and served on everything from battleship to submarine. He began to show his stuff back in 1925, when he displayed considerable cold fatted calves, but it is surely nice while it lasts and the planes are pretty and very sleek too."

Putnam and his twelve Fighters were brought by a carrier to within flying distance of Wake, then they took off and landed on the island without incident. Nine pilots besides Putnam were commissioned. Two were enlisted men. Ground crews were at Wake already, and when the fighter squadron landed, the combined forces had three days left to get ready for what the Japs had in store.

Early on the morning of December 8, Wake time, the Marine garrison received a radio flash of the Pearl Harbor bombing. The alarm immediately called all hands to battle stations, and four Fighters began a constant patrol, being relieved by four more when their tour of duty was done.

When the Pearl Harbor flash came, the Philippine Clipper, which had just left for Guam, was recalled by radio. The Marines' commanding officer planned to have the Clipper make a reconnaissance patrol with two Marine Fighters as escorts. They were to leave at one o'clock that day. The flight never came off.

At two minutes of noon twenty-four Jap bombers, flying at 3000 feet, came in from the south. The Marine Corps ground forces, under Major James P. S. Devereux, opened up with anti-aircraft, but the planes came on and hit the airdrome hard, then continued north across the island to bomb Pan American Airways on near-by Peale Island, and returned to plaster the airdrome again.

The raid was over quickly, and in its wake were twenty-five dead and seven wounded of the Marines' aviation squadron. Of the eight Marine Fighters on the ground when the raid began, seven were completely destroyed, the other much damaged.

When the four Marine Fighters on patrol came down after the raid, one damaged a propeller when landing on the wreck-strewn field, which left only three planes ready

Major Paul A. Putnam, U.S.M.C.

to take the air. But the Marines had a grand repair crew. Working all night under command of Lieutenant John F. Kinney and Sergeant William J. Hamilton, they had the two damaged planes ready before dawn; then they began stripping the wrecked planes for parts that could be used again.

Next day, the 9th, the Japs came again, this time at a quarter to twelve noon. Twenty-seven twin-engined bombers dropped their loads on Camp 2 of the contractor's men, and also plastered the island's small hospital, killing three patients.

When the twenty-seven bombers came in sight, they were attacked by the four Marine Fighters, and one bomber rolled over to come down in flames. Three of the Marine aviation men were killed by bombs or strafing.

On the 10th, this time at 10:45 A.M., the Japs arrived with twenty-seven bombers again. They unloaded and did some damage, but inflicted no casualties. By this time the defenders had built ground shelters, well covered and showing no light, in which men could repair planes night and day, and sleep close to their work.

By now, too, the Japs must have thought they had softened up the island's defenders. On the 11th they came in for the kill. At five o'clock that morning, Marine lookouts gave the alarm. Coming in from the southwest was a sizable Jap fleet. When it got near enough, it was seen to contain twelve vessels, including a cruiser, destroyers, gunboats, and two transports or supply ships. It was obvious that the enemy had come fully prepared and expecting to land on Wake.

Major Devereux and his ground force had been working hard. Wake is not, as so often reported, a bare piece of ground. There is much brush, and many hardwood trees, that afford excellent cover. Devereux had used this cover to advantage, and now with an enemy fleet coming in, the snouts of Marine 3-inch and 5-inch artillery pointed unobtrusively from behind thick clumps of bushes. Meantime, the Marines' four remaining Fighters climbed high in the sky.

At 6,000 yards the Jap cruiser opened fire. Major Devereux had ordered his artillery to hold their fire until he gave the word. On steamed the fleet, now pounding with all its guns. The range closed to 5,500 yards, but no Marine gun answered. It closed to 5,000 yards and ceased a moment while the enemy flagship ran up a group of signals. A Marine came to Major Devereux.

"They are signaling us to surrender, sir," he reported.

"Tell them to come and get us," the Major replied.

The flags came down, the Jap guns resumed their pounding, and the range closed to 4,700 yards. Devereux gave the command.

Instantly the brush cover all around blazed as the Marines opened fire.

Coming down from 15,000 feet, the four Grumman Fighters began bombing, concentrating on the cruiser. Two of the Marine planes, piloted by Captains Elrod and Tharin, hit the Jap cruiser with eight 100-pound bombs. She started burning at once, then settling by the bows, and a wildly joyous audience saw her sink, right then and there.

The artillery was hitting things too. They were pouring it into two destroyers and a gunboat. The gunboat was the first to go down. Ten minutes later a destroyer heaved, listed, and went under. Within another half-hour a second destroyer, its crew leaping wildly in all directions, turned half over, then went down by the stern.

It was swell shooting and bombing. The Jap fleet pulled away, one of its remaining ships trailing smoke as she went over the horizon.

Major Devereux of the ground force, Major Putnam of

the air squadron, and Major Walter L. J. Bayler, on temporary duty in charge of ground-air communications, immediately prepared for another assault by the enemy, which came that same day.

The Japs had learned one lesson: The Wake defenders were not to be taken simply by coming in with a fleet and landing—not yet, anyway. One Jap cruiser, two destroyers, and one gunboat had gone down in the first landing attempt. In the second attack on the 11th, which began about noon, the Jap fleet kept well out of range, and sent in a large force of bombers.

The Marines' anti-aircraft began banging away, and the four Grummans went aloft. Captain Elrod's plane was shot out of commission and he had to make a crash landing on the beach, his plane a total loss. Captain Freuler took some armor-piercing bullets through his plane engine, but landed safely. Five minutes later the tireless Lieutenant Kinney and Sergeant Hamilton and their crews were trying to patch it up for another flight.

The Marine anti-aircraft had a good day of it. They hit and brought down two Jap bombers.

There was no rest. Next day, the 12th, twenty-seven bombers came in, at 22,000 feet, and plastered the island systematically, but did little damage. Late that afternoon, Lieutenant Kliewer, up on patrol, sighted something new offshore. It was a Jap sub, the first seen in the vicinity. Kliewer dove at the sub, turning loose with his 50-caliber gun. As he pulled out of his dive, he let his two bombs go. Both were hits, fair enough, and the sub sank.

The Japs were paying for what they got, and they hadn't got it yet. A Navy radio man at Pearl Harbor, talking with a Marine operator on Wake, jokingly asked what the Wake boys would like for Christmas.

"Send us more Japs," the Marine replied, in the best

Marine tradition, and millions of Americans at home knew that twenty years of peace hadn't softened the sea-soldiers very much.

On Saturday the 13th no Jap, either on, above, or under the sea, was seen to approach the hornets' nest of Wake. But on Sunday they made up for the rest. Thirty-two Jap planes returned, flying at 22,000 feet again. They hit the airdrome fair, but effected no damage elsewhere. As the four Grumman Fighters went up to meet the armada, one crashed at the take-off. No Grummans or Japs were shot down; but the accident left the Marines with only three good planes.

There was no let-up. The Japs were determined. By moonlight that night, two big seaplanes came in on a raid, but they seemed to be confused and went away after dropping their loads harmlessly in a lagoon. Eight hours later twenty-seven bombers returned, and today they were running into trouble. The three little Grummans went up like tiny birds attacking eagles and ten minutes later, after doing some miraculous shooting and maneuvering, they shot two of the bombers into the sea.

The day would have been practically perfect had it not been for another accident. A Grumman going up for patrol crashed on the take-off. That left two planes to the Marines.

The defense of Wake, even though its defenders were far too busy to think of it in that light, was fast becoming one of the very great pages of American fighting history. In conserving powder and equipment until the enemy was well within range, in making every shot count, it ranked with Bunker Hill. In its elements of Last Stand desperation, it was an Alamo. Major Devereux and his men were fit to stand with General Warren and his farmers; Major Putnam's little squadron, the peer of Davy Crockett's crew. Moreover, on December 16th, after a week of heavy and almost constant fighting, Wake was still taking it and dishing it out.

Major James P. S. Devereux, U.S.M.C.

At half-past noon of the 16th the Japs sent in what they must have been certain was the final blow, the last round, the one that precedes the triumphal entry. It came in the form of forty-one bombers. They blew up a dynamite dump on Wilkes Inlet. They shot the storehouse to pieces and burned it flat. They wiped out the machine shop, the black-smith shop, and hit nearly every building of any kind on the island. Neither the two Grummans nor the anti-aircraft brought down a single Jap. But the day wasn't quite over. At half-past five that afternoon, a lone four-engined patrol came in to drop some more bombs uselessly in the lagoon. Captain Tharin went up with the next-to-last Grumman and, by God, he shot it down in flames.

It must have been a heartbreaking fight, those two hellish weeks on Wake. Officers and men must have cried for a few more planes, just a few, knowing they could hold out until kingdom come if only they had the stuff to fight with. But they couldn't have had much time to think on the matter. On the 17th a flight of thirty-two Japs hit the Diesel oil dump, exploding it to burn for hours. They also hit the defense ground force's tent camp, hard.

On the 18th there was no bombing. In midday, though, a lone Jap was seen to fly over the island, very high and in a straight line. Major Putnam knew the signs; the Jap was taking pretty photographs.

On the 19th a heavy flight of bombers returned, this time to concentrate on the wooded area south of the airfield. The Jap, looking at the aerial pictures, no doubt decided that the woods were filled with Marine planes. The Marines wished to God they had been.

Bad weather came down over Wake on the 20th. A Navy patrol plane had flown in during the night, and it now left Wake carrying Major Bayler and a detailed report of action during the previous twelve days.

All that came out of Wake after the 20th was a series of

terse dispatches, which ceased on the 22nd. They told of a big attack on the 22nd. The last two Marine Fighters went up as usual. Captain Freuler, pilot of one, was wounded and had to make a crash landing. A lieutenant whose name was not released took off in the other Fighter. "He did not return," said the dispatch.

It had taken a Jap fleet and air force two weeks to accomplish the fall of Wake Island. To take it cost a cruiser, two destroyers, a gunboat, a submarine, a four-engined seaplane, nine bombers, and possibly three more bombers, besides an unknown number of Jap dead and wounded. And these figures do not include destruction which the cornered Marines must have done during that last grim battle on the 22nd.

What losses the Marine ground forces suffered is not known. The Marine air squadron, up to the 22nd, lost twenty-eight men, and six wounded.

On January 5, President Roosevelt, in a special order, cited the Wake Detachment of the First Marine Defense Battalion and Marine Fighting Squadron 211 of Marine Aircraft Group 21.

Who were these brave men of Wake? The Navy hasn't said, except in the case of the two commanding officers. Major James Patrick Sinnot Devereux (spelled two ways in official Marine Corps reports) was born in Cuba in 1903, educated in Washington, D. C., and Lucerne, Switzerland, and enlisted in the Marines in 1923. He was commissioned second lieutenant, served on ships, and at Shanghai, Peking, and Pearl Harbor. In 1933 he attended the coast artillery school at Fort Monroe, a course that stood him ably when he saw the Jap fleet coming in at Wake.

Four months after the Battle of Wake, Major Devereux's wife, and son John, eight, stood in Times Square, New York, to unveil the first of several thousand posters to promote a fund for the United Service Organizations. And on May 16, Major Devereux's family received welcome news through the International Red Cross: "Major James P. S. Devereux is alive and well in Shanghai, a prisoner of war."

Wherever he is, stands a gallant man.

Major Paul Albert Putnam, like Devereux, was born in 1903, but in Milan, Michigan. He enlisted in the Marines in 1923, was later commissioned, and went in for flying. He served on various stations, and during the Nicaraguan campaign was cited for bravery. Major Putnam's wife and their three children are living in California.

Presumably a prisoner of the Japs, Major Putnam has a safe niche in the lore of Marines and in the hearts of his fellow Americans, as the man who fought the enemy, not to the last ditch, but literally to the last plane.

"Don't fire until you can see the whites of their eyes."

COLONEL WILLIAM PRESCOTT,
BUNKER HILL, 1775.

12

PATWING TEN'S LIFE AND TIMES

The second pilot shouted over the phones of the Navy Patrol bomber: "There are twelve Japs dead ahead. Man your guns." The guns began chattering, sweeping the Jap Zeros, and the Navy pilot started the plane into a dive straight down from 12,000 feet. A second or two later Clarence Bannowsky, third pilot, looked out a side window and saw that a greater part of the wing surfaces had been shot away.

The plane's commander ordered a bail-out. Four of the bomber's crew went over the side in their chutes. Bannowsky didn't jump. He looked aft and saw that the other crew members were not going to be able to make it, to bail out.

"Maybe I can land her on the water," Bannowsky said as he sat down at the controls.

Jap bullets were ripping through the bomber from both sides, and the bomber's gunners were hitting the Japs.

As Bannowsky brought the plane down near the sea, he suddenly jolted forward in his seat and pain raced up and down his back as though from the stab of a hot knife. He had just got a Jap bullet not far below the shoulders.

Hanging on to his seat and the controls, Bannowsky took the plane for a landing on the sea. "Prepare to abandon ship," he shouted, then, "Help me out of this jacket. I'm hit."

They got the third pilot out of his jacket, bloody by now, and then tossed the rubber boat into the water. The gunners kept up a fire until the last moment.

Splashing into the sea, the crew headed for the rubber boat, but now the Japs circled and dived, strafing at every head that showed.

"Swim around and duck," Bannowsky said. "Duck as much as you can. Keep away from the boat."

The crew swam apart, all keeping a distance from the bobbing rubber boat, and meanwhile the Japs kept coming and shooting, first with guns, then with cannon. The Navy boys ducked and swam as long as they could, but finally they tired. They just floated and watched, completely helpless to do anything about the Japs. The rubber boat still floated.

This went on for twenty minutes, then the Japs flew off. The exhausted Navy boys swam to their boat, which they found still seaworthy, and got in. Not far away they could see their good old bomber in flames and preparing to sink.

They made land all right, a small island off the Java coast, and there found the four crew members who had bailed out. Not a man had been killed. It was the miraculous luck, so far as men were concerned, that seemed to hover over the crews of Patwing Ten during all of its ninety hectic days of life.

The story of Patwing Ten, however, is not one that will lend itself to orderly narrative. Its brief life span began in the Philippines and closed in Australia, with Java in between, and it was far too feverish for one correspondent to cover, or a dozen. Its crews were too busy making history to record it. Ragged and devious, filled with hit-and-run murder, with hopeless but telling battle against terrible

Aviation Machinist Mate 2/c Clarence J. Bannowsky, Jr.

odds, it amounts to being the Odyssey of a Navy outfit that started life with forty-two bombers and ended with two bullet-riddled crates. Yet, six out of every seven men survived an almost constant air-guerrilla warfare that lasted from December 8 to early March of 1942.

Patwing Ten saw its first action on the morning of December 8 (the 7th at Pearl Harbor) near an advanced base in the Philippines, when a detachment was ordered to investigate a report of a fleet of Jap warships off the coast of Luzon. The patrol found the fleet, which contained two battleships of the Kongo class and four destroyers.

The Navy boys got into the sun, then started in for the bombing run. They dropped fifteen tons of stuff on one of the big ships to what Chief Machinist's Mate Mike Kelly thought was very good advantage. Then the Navy planes scattered to hide in the clouds and to resume formation later. Not a plane was lost.

Cavite was being used at this time as a base for Patwing Ten, but Cavite got too hot. The wing split up, to base at obscure spots from which they could run and hit, then return. The Japs kept finding their hide-outs, driving them out, and in a little while it was usual for a Navy plane to start out on a mission with no idea whence it would go from there. In spite of these conditions the boys managed to get in a lot of telling fighting.

Their toughest luck came on December 27. A Jap cruiser and several destroyers and transports were reported approaching Luzon without fighter escort. It sounded like a swell chance, and a Patwing Ten group set out. They came up with the Jap fleet in early dawn. Then, in Chief Kelly's words:

"We started in on a bombing run, and the machine gunner aft in my plane reported fighters above, plenty of them. They started to dive on us immediately, but we held to our course and went in to bomb the vessels below.

"The other section of our squadron had already made a nice approach and dropped their bombs. We came in with fierce anti-aircraft fire breaking all around us. Yes, and some of it through us. Our gunners were keeping the Japs off as well as they could as we dived for the water.

"One plane in our section was shot down. A Jap made a run for us from underneath, and our tunnel gun knocked him off as pretty as you could imagine. The Japs must have concluded that was a bad spot—to come at us from underneath—so they changed tactics and attacked us from above.

"My plane and one other from my section got back to base. None of the other section returned. Four planes were lost."

Chief Machinist's Mate John Cumberland was in that other section, the lost one, and he lived to tell about it.

"We made a turn and came in over the Jap fleet," he says. "Then we ran for one of their destroyers. We bombed for a near-miss, then made another turn for altitude. Just then the enemy fighters came after us. One of them came in underneath the stabilizer. I held off until he got in good range, then fanned my string at him. It apparently did no good, for he came right back again, and with him were half-a-dozen others.

"They would make a run on our starboard, then on our port side. I hit one of them, a Zero, fair in the belly. Our own ship was filling up—with holes. By the time we got it down onto the water, most of the crew were gas-drunk from leakage.

"Well, we could still float. We plugged the holes in our plane and drifted around for thirty hours, when we were picked up by a rescue crew."

Every day or so Patwing Ten lost another plane. Few of its crew escaped at least one wound, and the boys still wonder how it was that Chief Machinist's Mate C. M.

Richardson got out of one particular scrape with only two wounds; by rights he should have been shot into shreds.

Mate Richardson's plane was followed to its base one night by enemy fighters who attacked the minute the American plane had landed on the water. Nine Japs came at the lone Navy ship. Richardson was at the bow turret gun and the Japs made their runs directly at him. The leading Jap passed and rocked its wings—a signal for the others to come in shooting. They did.

Richardson, his mates say, is a man who never shoots until he can see the slants of their eyes—a sort of modern Colonel William Prescott. Richardson waited that long and no longer. Dodging from side to side in his turret, he kept up such a hot fire that the Japs drew off, then went away. Richardson's machine gun had been shot away, and later more than seven hundred holes were counted in the Navy plane, most of them in and around the turret. That Richardson survived with one slight wound in one hand and another in the leg is something that Patwing Ten veterans will talk about at reunions for years to come.

Then there was the lone stand made on Christmas morning by Machinist's Mate Roland D. Foster. This notable incident is known to Patwing Ten boys as the Battle of the Turkey Dinner. It happened this way:

By Christmas all but one of the wing's surviving planes had been moved away from the Philippines. The remaining plane was based at Los Banos and was being used as an attack plane in the Bataan fighting, with Lieutenant H. R. Swenson in command.

On Christmas morning Lieutenant Swenson and the enlisted pilot, J. S. Clark, were ashore trying to buy a turkey from a native. Even a late turkey dinner would be better than none to men so far from home. But their shopping was interrupted by a radio warning that Jap planes were approaching. Swenson and Clark struck back for the beach where their plane was moored. They saw three Jap fighters swarming around the Navy plane and could hear their guns. They also heard the Navy plane's guns firing back, and assumed that the crew was aboard and fighting.

"We could easily see that our plane's bow gun was going," says Lieutenant Swenson, "and so were the two waist guns. We crept closer. Just then the bow gun ceased firing. We figured our gunner must have been hit, so we took it on the lam for the plane with the idea of relieving the wounded gunner. The Japs fired at us but we were not hit."

When Swenson and Clark got inside their plane, they also got the surprise of their lives. Only one man was on board. He was a mechanic, Roland D. Foster, and he was a man to be reckoned with. Foster was keeping the 50-caliber guns going in the port waist and the twin 30's going in the starboard waist. It was an almost incredible performance.

"When the Japs would approach," Swenson related, "Foster would open up with the 50-caliber, and as they passed he would switch to the 30-caliber on the starboard side. He ran out of 30-caliber ammunition and ran up to the bow to get more. While he was in the bow, the Japs made another run at him. He simply turned the bow gun loose on them.

"On the way back to the waist guns he discovered that Jap bullets had set fire to a mattress. But this didn't worry him, for the many bullet holes in our hull had let five inches of water into the after compartment. Foster rigged the bilge pump, squirted water on the mattress, then went back to his guns.

"When Clark and I came aboard Foster was going from gun to gun, and on the last pass of the Japs he shot one of their guns out of commission and hit one of their engines hard enough to stop it. That put two Japs out of the fighting. The other circled around once, then went home. Too much Foster for him."

When the Japs had gone Lieutenant Swenson took stock.

Aviation Machinist Mate 3/c C. M. Richardson

There were 265 holes in the plane. The parts around the gun stations looked like sieves. One shell from a cannon had made a 16-inch hole in the after starboard gas tank. The radio compartment had two holes in the bottom. The wings were shredded here and there.

It was time to get away from *that* base, and Swenson wondered if the battered plane could make the run of eighty miles to Cavite, where repairs could be made. He urged his crew to go by land, but they stuck to the ship to a man. They turned to and plugged such holes as they could, and applied haywire elsewhere, then they started the engines.

It was going to be quite a voyage. Ensign Williamson was standing in the navigation compartment—in eighteen inches of water. The night was cloudy, visibility was very poor. The sea was heavy. Mate Butterbaugh reported the engines warmed and ready for the take-off. Pilot Clark shoved the throttles full forward, or four inches above the rated take-off power, and the plane started her run.

They held her close to the water for a time to see if she was going to act all right. She started out pretty fair, everything considered, so they started their climb. Just then Lieutenant Swenson got a message over the plane's interphone. It was from Foster, at one of the waist guns.

"Mr. Swenson," said Foster, "there's gasoline leaking back here."

"Got to let her leak," said Swenson.

Another message came over the interphone, this time from Cox, the second radioman.

"Mr. Swenson, sparks are coming out of the engine."

"Thanks," said Swenson, "Okay."

The next message came from Butterbaugh at the engine controls:

"Mr. Swenson, we are losing oil from the port engine."

"Aye, aye," said Swenson.

By now they had got the wreck up to about 1,800 feet, and they leveled off, going cross country toward Cavite. Butterbaugh kept reporting the loss of oil in the port engine—forty gallons left, then thirty, then ten, and finally: "Mr. Swenson, we have no oil in the port engine."

When the pressure was gone Swenson turned off the port engine.

That was the way they came into Cavite, one engine silent, the other coughing and roaring by turns. They made a good landing on the Bay and taxied two miles with one engine to Cavite Navy Base. They were feeling pretty darned good, but they didn't realize what had been going on at Cavite.

The moment they got to shore they knew something unusual was up. Men were running here and there. Orders were being barked over loud-speakers. Now and again a loud explosion would jar the ground. The new arrivals learned that the Americans were blowing up what was left of the Cavite air station and were getting out, right now, some for Bataan, others elsewhere.

There would be no chance to repair the Patwing plane here. So, its crew went down to the water and sank it. They just managed to leap aboard a tug as the gangplank was being lifted, and were taken to Mariveles on Bataan Peninsula for the next series of adventures in this particular part of Patwing Ten's squadron.

One hundred and thirty men of Patwing Ten joined the MacArthur and Wainwright forces on Bataan, fighting as Marines under Commander Francis J. Bridget. The reason they fought as ground force was that they didn't have any planes.

Five weeks of hell, the hell that was all of Bataan, followed. Patwing Ten men fought Jap bombers from the ground with machine guns, living in fox holes, meanwhile

Lieutenant Harold R. Swenson, U.S.N.R.

weeping and cursing and praying for a dozen, even half a dozen, or even one of their beloved PBY ships. When the end of Bataan was seen to be near, the qualified pilots of Patwing Ten were taken to Corregidor, then flown to Java or Australia to resume fighting with planes in new units.

While part of the wing was fighting on Bataan, the major part of the wing had moved south, hedgehopping from island to island, operating in groups of two to six planes each, and sometimes alone. In Java the Dutch came through with six brand-new PBY's which helped to fill gaps. And an entire new squadron was brought in from Honolulu. These additions put new zip and power into Patwing Ten's ebbing life.

During the battle in Turkey Lane—Macassar Straits to the layman—men of Patwing Ten stalked Jap sea forces, knocked over a Zero now and again, and sometimes a Zero knocked off one of the PBY's. It was the same old story of far more Zeros than PBY's.

A sample of a Patwing Ten day was a flight piloted by Chief Aviation Machinist's Mate Van Bibber:

"We were off the coast of Celebes when a fighter dove on us. We were about 10,000 feet. We saw him coming in time to start sliding right toward him and just about the time he hopped us, we put our plane into a slipping dive. He overshot us. Every time he would start back for us, we'd repeat the dive.

"The Jap made four runs, firing as he passed over. The fourth time he must have been in a hurry, for he started to turn back on us too soon. This brought him right above our quarter—wide open for a Sunday shot. Our waist gunner filled the Jap's cockpit with bullets. The Jap at once fell off on a wing tip and started smoking. It rolled over and plunged down about a thousand feet before it burst into flames."

Part of the outfit got to Port Darwin, Australia, a few

days ahead of the first Jap raid there. On the morning of February 19, 1942, one hundred and eight Jap bombers came in from the southwest. Pilot H. R. Cannon was standing by a plane buoy on watch when he heard the mighty roar of the coming trouble.

Cannon and his mates manned a whaleboat and ran it to the beach across the bay from Port Darwin, mooring it under some trees. The bombs began to fall. Cannon could see Patwing Ten's mother ship, a tender, in the Bay, and also the U.S. Destroyer *Peary*. Both were getting under way to start zig maneuvers to dodge bombs—if they could.

They couldn't. "I saw a big bomb hit the *Peary* amidships," Cannon related. "There was a terrific explosion and the ship sank in five minutes or less, her captain, Lieutenant Commander John M. Bermingham, and many of her crew with her.

"Next bomb hit the tender, just forward of the after deckhouse on the port side. She caught fire. An ammunition ship alongside the dock began blowing up.

"Just at this time Lieutenant Commander Etheridge Grant, skipper of the tender, was making his way toward his ship in a small boat from the shore. He might have made it, but for the explosions of the ammunition ship. The blast lifted Grant's little boat up like a cork and turned it over. Grant grabbed a buoy and hung on."

There was Grant in the midst of bombs and machine gun fire, hanging to a bounding buoy. And there was his ship, the tender, in a like fix. The bomb had wrecked the tender's rudder control; her afterdeck was a blazing fury. But her anti-aircraft guns were throwing up a ring of steel and fire, and the boys were steering her by hand. With black smoke billowing from her funnels, the tender made for the open sea, fighting all the way, with Lieutenant L. O. Woods in command. He brought her to safety.

The Patwing Ten boys liked to think they had something

to do with saving the tender. Just before the raid they had taken the 50-caliber machine guns from wrecked PBY's and installed them on the decks of the tender, and the tender proved too hot a target for the Jap strafers.

But the days of Patwing Ten were almost over. Their planes knocked out one by one until only two remained, the outfit was broken up and its men transferred to other units.

Decorations or promotions were issued to fifty-seven officers and men of the gallant Naval aviation outfit. Captain Frank D. Wagner, of Washington, D. C., who commanded the wing during its early operations, was awarded the Distinguished Service Medal. The Distinguished Flying Cross went to Commander John V. Peterson, Omaha, Nebraska, who succeeded Wagner as wing commander.

The Navy Cross went to Lieutenants Burden R. Hastings, Quantico, Virginia, who is reported missing in action; Jack Baldwin Dawley, Seattle; Elwyn L. Christman, Mount Angel, Oregon; to Radioman Robert Lee Pettit, deceased, whose widow lives in Honolulu; and to other enlisted men as follows: Don Dexter Lurvey, San Diego, California, Joseph Bangust, deceased, of Milwaukee, Andrew K. Walderman, San Diego, deceased, and Everen C. McLawhorn, La Grange, North Carolina.

Distinguished Flying Crosses were awarded to Lieutenants Harmon T. Utter, Neville, Ohio, Clarence A. Keller, Arlington, Virginia, Charles C. Hoffman, Honolulu, Duncan Angus Campbell, Grand Rapids, Minnesota, LeRoy C. Deede, Woodworth, North Dakota, Richard Bull, deceased, Macomb, Illinois, John M. Robertson, missing, Los Angeles, William S. Robinson, missing, Zamboanga, P. I., Ira W. Brown, Jr., Ottumwa, Illinois; and to Ensign John F. Davis, Evansville, Indiana.

Enlisted men of Patwing Ten who received promotions "for meritorious conduct" are as follows:

Clarence J. Bannowsky, North Long Beach, California; Dave Wesley Bounds, Los Angeles; Wilmot Eiler Bowen, Mountain Lake Park, Maryland; John William Clark, Fairhope, Alabama; Maynard E. Humphreys, Morrow, Ohio; John Arden Wilson, Port Neches, Texas; Dayton W. Treat, missing, Wayland, New York; Michael D. Kelly, Mendham, New Jersey; John L. Cumberland, Culver, Kansas; Mario Ferrara, Wakefield, Massachusetts; Edgar P. Palm, San Carlos, California; N. T. Whitford, Vanceboro, North Carolina; Lindsey B. Wells, New Bern, North Carolina; Ralph W. Preece, San Diego; Charles J. Pozanac, missing, San Francisco; John W. Bilsky, Ansonia, Connecticut; Henry C. Gudikunst, Ephrata, Pennsylvania; Michael George Irano, Stamford, Connecticut; John Winfred Jones, Bauxite, Arkansas; Ford S. Kelley, Brighton, Colorado; Sandy Bolin, Brent, Florida; Phillip S. Perry, Maywood, California; Bedlington N. Wood, Jr., San Francisco; John M. Leaverton, missing, Greeley, Colorado; Thomas L. Vinson, Sioux City, Iowa; Charles R. Phillips, Jr., St. Louis, Missouri; Bernard C. Nichols, Long Pine, Nebraska; William R. Miller, Pittsburg, Kansas; Paul H. Landers, missing, Granite City, Illinois; Claude A. Grant, Mars Hill, Maine; Horace P. Garrett, Jr., Collinsville, Alabama; Russell J. Enterline, San Francisco; Lyle H. Dudgeon, Audubon, Iowa; Olan L. Dockery, Los Angeles; Rosario A. Caltabiano, Ocean Park, California; Carlton C. Chestnut, Troup, Texas; Dean Perry, Lohrville, Iowa.

Bangust, Pettit, and Walderman lost their lives fighting over the Philippines. McLawhorn was wounded seven times but survived to fight again. He manned both waist guns alternately when gunners at these points in his plane were killed. "Enemy incendiaries," says the Navy, "ignited a number of ammunition cases in the plane and machine

Mission Accomplished: A Patwing Ten plane returns home

gun bullets in the boxes began to explode. The wounded man jettisoned the exploding cases, risking his own life in so doing."

"Pettit," says the Navy, "refused to leave his station when his compartment was flooded with gasoline, although to have done so would have saved his life. Enemy bullets subsequently ignited the gasoline and he was killed."

Bangust and Walderman died at their gunner's posts. Lurvey risked his life to save his pilot from drowning when his plane crashed.

Typical, however, of the work that won promotions for the Patwing Ten men was the kind of thing related in the citations of Gudikunst, Jones, Bilsky, Perry, Dudgeon, Enterline, and Vinson:

"For his courageous, efficient and unflagging performance of duty during the week 8-15 December, 1941. Throughout this week, under the most trying conditions and in the face of daily heavy bombing attacks, he was outstanding in his manner of performance of duty. By diligence, ingenuity, and long hours of overwork, he was an important factor in maintaining communications of a most vital nature, despite numerous and repeated obstacles of excessive traffic load, failure and loss of material, and the most trying conditions of operation."

There, in that citation, is the kind of grubby, difficult, and "non-heroic" work the public seldom thinks about. It is the kind of work, of teamwork, of responsibility to duty, that made the brilliant record of Patwing Ten possible. It never brings medals unless other factors are present. But it often calls for as much guts as a fighting man can display anywhere. It calls always for stamina and determination. It is also the kind of work which, when performed as well as Patwing Ten's men performed it, indicates a high degree of mechanical ability—in a war fought largely by machines a pretty good quality to have.

All glory to Patwing Ten's men who received decorations and to those who didn't.

The roster of Patwing Ten indicates men with English, Scotch, Welsh, Irish, Dutch, German, Italian, Scandinavian, Russian, and Czech blood in their veins, and their record indicates them to be Americans of the first water.

They came from all parts of the United States and its possessions. California contributed twelve men to Patwing Ten. Iowa, four. Three each came from North Carolina and Texas. Two each came from Nebraska, Virginia, Ohio, Illinois, Alabama, Kansas, Connecticut, Colorado, and the Territory of Hawaii. One came from each of the following states: Washington, Oregon, Wisconsin, Minnesota, North Dakota, Indiana, Maryland, New York, New Jersey, Massachusetts, Pennsylvania, Arkansas, Florida, Missouri, and Maine. The Philippine Islands had one man in the group, and the group's first commander came from the District of Columbia.

The fighting record of Patwing Ten will doubtless fall into shadow again and again before the war is over. That is what happens to fighting records, for memory is short and events come crowding so fast there is not room for everything. Yet, when all the smoke of the war has settled and the writers of history books begin their task, the ninety-day battle of Patwing Ten should find a place in their pages.

"We have met the enemy and they are ours."

COMMODORE OLIVER H. PERRY,
LAKE ERIE, 1813.

13

THE WORDS OF FIGHTING MEN

SCARCELY MORE THAN once or twice in a war does a spoken sentence emerge from the smoke of battle to be remembered. It is then repeated over and over by old soldiers, printed in books, and often etched in bronze and marble. It isn't always easy to tell what makes such a sentence remembered, although the quality of phrases credited to certain Americans in the Revolutionary War is such that they cannot be forgotten.

At times Army men have made the best phrases. Again it is the salty line of some old sea dog. One of the very best lines ever spoken by an American fighting man was uttered by Captain Parker on Lexington Green in Massachusetts, the one that ends: ". . . but if they mean to have a war, let it begin here." Somehow, those old farmers and backwoodsmen appear to have had a gift for unforgettable phrases. Less than a month after Captain Parker spoke, Colonel Ethan Allen was demanding surrender of a fort "In the name of the great Jehovah and the Continental Congress." And presently Colonel William Prescott, at Bunker's Hill, was showing good generalship and at the same time speaking a line all Americans know. "Don't fire," he told his farmers, his squirrel-rifle men, "until you can see the whites of their eyes."

All of these were Army men. In the War of 1812, however, when our Navy was active, it was Navy men who said the things remembered. A great slogan was Commodore Oliver H. Perry's "We have met the enemy and they are ours." So were Captain James Lawrence's dying words: "Don't give up the ship!"

It was an admiral who contributed the one line that is remembered from the Battle of Mobile Bay. When his advance squadron was held up, David Farragut, high in the rigging of his flagship, was a good deal put out. "What's wrong there?" he shouted through his trumpet.

"Torpedoes," came the answer.

"Damn the torpedoes! Full speed ahead," the old sea dog roared.

The taciturn Grant seldom spoke more than a few words at a time, but his lines were very good, all the way from his "unconditional surrender" to "I propose to fight it out on this line if it takes all summer."

In a later war, that of 1898, Admiral George Dewey uttered a simple phrase, merely an order, that went into the history books, although the reasons for its immortality are certainly not inherent in the words themselves. They were, in fact, particularly colorless. Dewey was on the bridge of his flagship, the *Olympia*, in Manila Bay. The Spaniards had just begun shooting. Dewey turned to his flag captain and said: "You may fire when you are ready, Mr. Gridley." A week later those words were being repeated by millions of Americans and they reappear in almost any account of that battle, or even of that war.

Apparently nothing genuine, nothing spontaneous, came out of America's part in the first World War, so far as a historic phrase is concerned, although one synthetic line is remembered, and one other line, a rank piece of plagiarism, is often quoted.

When General John Pershing arrived in France in 1917 he laid a wreath on the grave of Lafayette. Pershing was a man of few and uncommonly uninteresting words. The chances are very great that he didn't say anything at all when he paid America's homage to the great Frenchman. But a newspaperman felt the weight of the moment and felt the need for a good resounding line, so presently the cables reported Black Jack to have said, in French to boot: "Lafayette, we are here." It went very well with the public.

The other line of that war has been credited to a number of American soldiers, usually a Marine sergeant who, at Belleau Wood, is supposed to have turned to his platoon and shouted: "Come on, you so-and-so's, do you want to live forever?" Almost the identical expression was credited, by no less than Thomas Carlyle, to the great Bismarck.

The present war, so far as the United States armed forces are concerned, is yet young. It may bring out a few lines equal to those in our history books. As this is written, the report of at least one American aviator appears sure of a place. David Francis Mason, a 28-year-old enlisted man of Rochester, Minnesota, was the indubitable author of it.

Flying a Navy plane, Machinist's Mate Mason on February 26, 1942, observed the wake of a submarine proceeding submerged at periscope depth, somewhere in the South Pacific. "Mason turned, " says the Navy's communiqué, "dove to a low altitude, and dropped two depth bombs, straddling the periscope. The conning tower of the sub bounded clear of the water for a short period and then sank. A large patch of oil soon appeared on the surface."

That was that one, Mason's first sub, but it wasn't the historic one.

A month later, while making a routine patrol flight, Mason, now advanced to the rank of chief aviation machinist's mate and wearing the Distinguished Flying Cross, observed another submarine, this one moving along on the surface. He swooped down and released his depth charges. All scored hits and the sub blew up in a mass of wreckage.

Then, from his homeward-bound plane, Mason radioed the terse, alliterative message that caught the press's fancy, then that of the public, and made Mason a marked man for life. Radioed Machinist's Mate Mason: "Sighted sub. Sank same."

It was a good line, covering the action competently. Mason says he gave no thought to its wording. It came out —just like that. For sinking the second sub, the Navy made Mason an ensign and gave him a Silver Star, equivalent to a second Distinguished Flying Cross.

This might be a good place to direct attention to a phrase uttered by another American fighting man in this war. Lieutenant Commander Frank W. Fenno, U. S. N., was the man. In the dark of Manila Bay, one night, just when all the gold from Corregidor had been transferred to Fenno's submarine and he was ready to push off on the long dangerous cruise to Pearl Harbor, Lieutenant Commander Fenno stood in his conning tower. Just before he gave the order to submerge, he asked a question of the officials who had filled his sub with gold:

"Any passengers?" he said, then closed his conning tower and let his ship sink into the dark waters.

"... that Congress award Dr. Walker a bronze medal for conspicuous service and bravery under fire."

CITING DR. MARY EDWARDS WALKER
FOR CIVIL WAR SERVICE.

14

YOUNG WOMEN AT WAR

SLIM, DARK-EYED Monica E. Conter, twenty-eight, was one of the two Army nurses on duty that morning in Station Hospital, close by Hickam Field at Honolulu. She and Miss Boyd had gone on duty at seven; other nurses were due at eight.

Just before eight o'clock Miss Conter heard the roaring of airplanes, which was nothing new at Hickam Field. But the roar went on and it ended in an explosion that shook the thirty-bed hospital as it had never shaken before.

Miss Conter ran out on the third-floor porch overlooking Pearl Harbor. She saw the air filled with planes that were not American. They were diving, and after every dive huge clouds of smoke rolled high, and a second later would come the crashing noise and jar of things being blown up.

One of the few patients had followed the nurse to the porch. He must have been an easygoing fellow, one not to be roused from his torpor by anything less than an earthquake, for after gazing at the scenes of destruction before his eyes, he remarked genially: "So, they're having maneuvers again."

He had scarcely delivered this observation when the Japs came over Hickam Field, right next door. A moment later came a shock that stopped every clock in the hospital and rolled every patient out of bed.

Miss Conter did not remain to hear the man change his mind about maneuvers. She tore downstairs as fast as she could go, got permission from her commanding officer, then tore up to the third floor again to start moving her patients to the ground floor.

The other nurses came hurrying on duty, and there was plenty to do. Hickam Field had taken a terrible beating and the first casualties were coming in, right from the hospital's front yard. Some of the cases were in such shape that Lieutenant Conter said later she could not find words to describe their condition. The uproar outside was still going on. Everyone had to yell to make himself heard four feet away. The nurses were moving fast and all of the early casualties were tagged (with instructions as to what treatment had been given them).

Now someone yelled: "Down, everybody!" All hands dropped to the floor, and the building vibrated from a new roaring of planes. Closer and closer they came, and then—

The world seemed to blow up. Things came flying through the windows. Bottles leaped from shelves to crash on the floor. The ground quaked. The hospital quaked. Through the shattered windows the flames of near-by buildings could be seen.

Somebody shouted "Gas!" and Miss Conter saw smoke or what looked like smoke come drifting in through doors and windows.

None had a gas mask or even a helmet—a condition typical of the time and place—until the attacks were over.

When the second flight of Japs had gone over, the nurses and doctors got to their feet and began a desperate twenty-four hours of work. The second stream of wounded, Miss

Conter noted, was even worse than the first, if that were possible. And there wasn't time to tag them all. They were brought in until the hospital beds and floors were covered with them; then they were laid on the grass in the hospital yard.

Hickam Field was still burning when additional aid began reaching the hospital. Red Cross and registered nurses came from Honolulu. The wives of Army and Navy officers, some of them with nursing experience, arrived. So did the wives of noncoms, petty officers, privates, and sailors. They turned to, to make dressings by the thousands.

Water was brought to the hospital in GI cans, and soon the mess started functioning. Those volunteer nurses who could be spared became cooks and waitresses.

When Lieutenant Conter took time out for a cup of coffee and a sandwich early that evening, the sun was just setting over tragic Pearl Harbor. She noted that directly in front of the hospital Old Glory was flying, though it had a huge rip completely across the stripes, due to machine gunning, and there were several shell craters a few feet from the base of the mast.

It made Miss Conter feel better to see the Flag there, and she returned to the wards to work through as bloody a night as any nurse is likely to remember. Her father, August E. Conter, M. D., back in small Apalachicola, Florida, could have reason to be proud of her.

White-haired First Lieutenant Florence MacDonald of Brockton, Massachusetts, was head nurse at Fort Stotsenburg hospital near Manila. For two days after December 8 she and her fifteen nurses worked steadily with only one catnap each, caring for the five hundred casualties from Clark Field. On the 24th they were ordered to evacuate all their patients to Manila then undergoing a continuous bombing.

The nurses followed the patients, and had Christmas Day in the doomed city, which had two air raids that day. On the 26th, nurses and patients were taken by steamer to Limay on Bataan, noting big fires at Cavite and Nichols Field as they cleared the harbor.

Limay hospital had been a barracks for the 45th Infantry. Now it was converted into seventeen wards of thirty beds each. The beds were already filling up with wounded of the 27th Cavalry which had so bravely covered the retreat to Bataan.

But Lieutenant MacDonald was still on the move. She was ordered to pack up and go to Corregidor.

She arrived on the Rock during the tremendous bombings of late December, and took up her position in Topside hospital in Corregidor. She remained at Topside until it was bombed so hard no one could stay there and live. She then took her nurses and patients into the deep Melinta tunnel, down low inside the Rock, and there for almost four months Lieutenant Mac carried on under the steady thudding of bombs.

The nurses at Limay were meanwhile having some experiences. One day the Japs bombed a native village right next to the hospital, and furnished scores of Filipino men, women, and children as patients. The Japs kept coming, more of them, every day, every night. By January 23, Limay was getting too hot to hold. Lieutenant Dorothea Mae Daley of Hamilton, Missouri, and other nurses at Limay were told to get their patients ready for evacuation and prepare to leave themselves.

Some of the doctors and nurses went to Cabcaben, others, including Miss Daley, to Little Baguio. This latter was simply a place in the jungle, although it was officially known as Hospital Number Two. Cots were strung out under trees and bushes. There wasn't a tent in the neighborhood, only a few shelter halves, pup tents. But there were plenty of mosquito bars, which at that time were more needed than tents.

The nurses' quarters consisted of a piece of burlap hanging on bamboo poles, with a sign: "Nurses Quarters. Ring Bell Before Entering." The nurses took ten grains of quinine daily. They ate when they could, and napped the same way. Their laundry and bath was a portion of the stream that ran its murky way through camp. It was dirty. It was crawling with leeches—black blood-suckers—and all sorts of bugs and slimy things. In it the nurses bathed and washed their clothes. Just above the spot the same stream was used by some 6,000 civilians for bathing and washing purposes.

The open-air hospital contained 3,600 beds, none covered with else but the shadow of trees. At the peak load there were 7,000 patients. The doctors managed to rig up a sort of tent operating room which they could black out, in a measure, after dark. They conducted operations on a twenty-four-hour basis, and the nurses worked the same way, often around the clock. There was not, one nurse recalls, any demand made for double-time pay, or even for time-and-one-half.

No direct attacks were made on Number Two, but now and again a stray bullet would thud into a mattress; once an anti-aircraft dud shell struck a hospital corporal; and a cook was killed while at his work by stray shrapnel. But Number Two was nearing the end of its days.

On April 8, what had been desultory rifle and artillery fire grew in intensity and sound. Along toward evening shells began bursting not far from the hospital. Just before dark the nurses were told to get ready to leave and to take only what they could carry in their hands.

The patients didn't know the nurses were going away, but the doctors and chaplains did. They sought out the girls to ask them to relay messages back to wives and mothers in the States, and loaded them with small trinkets to send to loved ones. Good-byes were said and a large and battered truck rolled in.

The truck was missing on several of its cylinders, but it would run and the Army sergeant at the wheel kept it rolling. Shells from Jap artillery were breaking in and near the road, which had never been much of a road anyway.

It was a wild night's ride, the truck bounding into and out of shell craters, the dark made lurid by fires on all sides, the air foul from the acrid smoke of explosives—and the nurses bouncing in the body of the truck, hanging on with both hands.

They got to Mariveles early in the morning, and then the nurses learned that Bataan had surrendered. They also learned that the boat that was to have taken them to Corregidor had left and that there probably wouldn't be any more boats; Japs were watching—and bombing—the Bay too closely and too much.

The nurses were there on the dock, but they were presently ordered away, told they couldn't stand there because the docks were sure to get another plastering from the skies. So the girls wandered off up the road and found a shady little nook. Lieutenant Daley discovered a perfectly good stone culvert, and into this she crept and had a fine nap.

Later that morning word came to the nurses that the boat was coming back for them. They rushed to the dock, and there sure enough was a boat, the little steamer *Mitchell*. While the girls were going aboard—almost as if this had been the moment—Jap planes came over and started to bomb. The boat pulled away with only twelve of the girls on deck—and the bombs came down, heavy and loud.

But nobody was hurt. The *Mitchell* returned to the dock and picked up the remaining nurses. The trip to The Rock was made without incident.

But Corregidor was undergoing a raid. Sirens were screeching as the girls landed. They were told to leave their baggage right there on the dock and to run up the hill as fast as they could go to the first tunnel entrance. The girls ran for dear life, while the ground, the rock, shook and the air was filled with flying pieces of bombs. All of them made it to the tunnel, but most of their baggage was destroyed during this raid by fires from incendiary bombs. Lieutenant Daley had nothing left but the coveralls she was wearing.

Another nurse who remained on Bataan until the last terrible days was Lieutenant Eunice Hatchett of Lockhart, Texas. In one of the open-air hospitals on Bataan she nursed the legendary Captain Arthur Wermuth, the One-Man-Army who, she said, usually had a new wound when he came near a hospital, although malaria got him once for a few days. Captain Wermuth was listed as missing a few days before Bataan fell, Miss Hatchett reported.

When Nurse Hatchett's group was evacuated from Bataan, it took them fifteen hours to travel the short distance from the hospital to the coast, much of it through area ablaze with ordnance and stores. On the way across to Corregidor their small boat was attacked once by dive-bombers.

Lieutenant Catherine Acorn, boyish, bob-haired nurse of Belmont, Mississippi, went through three evacuations under fire before she got to Corregidor. All beds in the Bataan hospitals had always held patients, she knew, and when she got to Corregidor she found the same conditions. During the last days on The Rock, all laterals in every tunnel were filled with wounded, she said—two to a bed in double-decked bunks.

On the Emperor's birthday, Miss Hatchett reported, the Japs let go at The Rock with everything. She could hear the bombs and shells thudding and exploding continuously all day. Smoke came into the tunnel entrances so thick that the nurses could hardly see to dress a wound or give a hypodermic. This went on for eight hours. "Or maybe it was eight years," Miss Hatchett said. On that day, she said, they had no more casualties than before, but perhaps that was because there were not enough stretcher-bearers to handle the wounded.

Lieutenant Willa Hook, late of Renfrow, Oklahoma, was on Corregidor when the war started. She volunteered and went to Bataan when the desperate January battles filled the jungle hospitals with Americans fighting a last-ditch stand. She went through two hospital bombings. Once she was working in a ward when another nurse cried out and fell to the floor—wounded by shrapnel while she was tending a wounded soldier.

Miss Hook said that conditions on Bataan just before it fell were pretty terrible. There were hundreds of gangrene cases, and all of the antigangrene serum had gone weeks before. So had all the sulfa drugs. So had all the quinine.

On April 7, while on duty at Hospital Number One on Bataan, Miss Hook and others of her group were knocked to the floor by a bomb that struck the Filipino mess hall a few yards away and blew it to bits, along with all it contained. Convalescent patients picked the girls up, and they now began taking care of the newly wounded, those who had been struck then and there by shell fragments, while the bedridden cases screamed and debris came through windows, or the places windows would have been.

A second bomb hit in this raid bounced the girls off the cement floor and threw them down again. One nurse was wounded. Beds swayed and tumbled, then collapsed with their patients. One little Filipino soldier with both legs amputated rolled over the floor to Miss Hook's side. "You all right?" he wanted to know. "You all right, Miss Hook?"

Miss Hook was dazed but all in one piece. She and the others got up again and set to work giving first aid to the already wounded who had been wounded a second time, and at least two patients who had been wounded a third time.

It was in this terrible hospital where Miss Hook happened to look up at her head ward nurse, Rosemary Hogan. She thought for a moment Miss Hogan's face had been torn off. It was all bloody. Miss Hook ran over. Nurse Hogan wiped her own face with a sheet. "Don't bother about me," she said. "Just a nose bleed. I get them sometimes." But Nurse Hogan had been hit by shrapnel three times.

During this bombing, an enlisted man ran into the ward that held the patients whose shattered legs were tied by ropes fastened to wires through the fractured bones. Better to hurt the patients temporarily than to leave them hog-tied during the raid, he thought. He cut all the ropes and told the patients to crawl under their cots. This brave action doubtless saved many lives and even more wounds, Miss Hook said.

Miss Hook and her group were finally sent back to Corregidor, where a big plane took them and several other Army nurses on the hop to Australia. But a number of Army nurses were on The Rock when it surrendered to the Japs, and they are now supposedly prisoners of war.

Miss Florence Nightingale and Miss Clara Barton would have been proud of the American girls at war in the South Pacific. So would have been tough old Doctor Mary Walker, who saw a good deal of battle in her time. They showed they could take it, along with American men, and they displayed the same courage as their brothers in arms. They came to believe, too, along with the fighting men they cared for, that courage is not enough to win wars.

"The soldiary behaved with uncommon ranker when they leaped into the fourt."

COLONEL ETHAN ALLEN,
CITING HIS TROOPS
AT TICONDEROGA, 1775.

15

BUZZ WAGNER GOES ALOFT

MANY ARMY AIR FORCE men say he is the best pursuit-plane pilot in the world, and his brother fliers who have seen him in action say he is a killer from way back. Not even Buzz Wagner himself knows how many enemy planes and men he has destroyed in the air, nor on the ground. The total number of Jap aircraft Wagner had disposed of up to early June of 1942 was certainly more than forty, and possibly ran to fifty.

In October of 1941, Boyd David Wagner, then twenty-four, was a first lieutenant in the Army Air Force. They made him a captain in the following January, and a lieutenant colonel in April. He is said to be the youngest wearer of silver leaves in all the Army, and he didn't win the leaves pushing papers across a desk nor did he owe them to any influence other than his superb technique as a flier and his deadly accuracy with a machine gun. Brother officers term Wagner an "H. P.," meaning "hot pilot," the greatest praise they can bestow.

Wagner was commanding a squadron of P-40's near

Manila when the war came. A week later the Japs started
to land in the Philippines and Wagner went out alone above
Aparri on reconnaissance. Tracer bullets suddenly began
going past his plane. They were coming from two Zero
fighters, much faster planes than the one the lone American
was driving. Turning into a steep climb Wagner got into the
sun, then went into a half-barrel roll and came down shooting. The two Zeros started smoking and flaming, then went
down for crash landings. Wagner had shot the guts out of
them.

That was fairly good for a beginning, Wagner thought,
and he was preparing to dig for home when he noticed for
the first time that he was just over a Jap airport, quite a
good-sized Jap airport. He was low enough to count an even
dozen Zero fighters nicely lined up on the field. It was too good
a chance for a man of Wagner's general disposition. Possibly he looked around to see if any more fighters were in
the air, and again maybe he didn't. What he did do was to
swoop down like a big hawk on a henyard. He turned on
his guns and swept over the field, setting two of the grounded
planes afire. Then he turned and came back, his guns going
again. He fired three more of the planes.

Just then three Japs attacked Wagner from above. They
had been away on a scouting trip, probably, and were returning home. They hopped right on the American. Wagner
dropped his empty belly tank and scooted for home, his plane
somewhat shot up but still serviceable.

A few days later Wagner in one pursuit and his pal Russell M. Church in another went on observation to see what the
Japs were doing at Vigan. They spotted a swell target—
twenty-five planes on the strip of a Jap airfield. The field
was well ringed with anti-aircraft, which immediately set
up a murderous fire around the two Americans. Bursts were
making the air look like a polka dot tie. The Americans paid
it no heed. First Wagner dived down, then Church.

Wagner leveled off directly above the grounded planes and came in on his run to release six fragmentation bombs, five making direct hits. Then he banked and climbed a bit while Church came in.

Two Jap fighters were close on Church's tail. They set his plane afire and Wagner expected every moment to see it go crashing down. Instead, Church came in over the field in a long, beautiful glide, and dumped his bombs as he went. He was manning his guns, too, strafing the ground crews.

But it was Church's last flight. Wagner saw his plane crash in flames just beyond the Jap airfield. Nobody jumped out of it.

Wagner's heart was choked up. He couldn't help his good pal now, but there was one thing he could do. He put his plane into a sharp dive and came in low with his guns spitting. He swept the field with its running men and its piles of smoking planes. He turned and dived again, going the entire length of the field. He swept back and forth five times before his ammunition gave out, then he went away home, heavyhearted. He had lost his closest friend. The Japs had lost thirty planes, and nobody but the Japs know how many men.

The loss of Church seemed to make Wagner more destructive to Japs than ever. He had learned a good deal about the fighting qualities of the Zeros, and even more about what he called "the terrific weapon" he himself was flying.

As a flier Wagner is a natural. He was made for it. His flying technique had been near perfect from the day he made his first solo flight; and it was now about as perfect as flying can be. Not that Wagner thought so, for he is rated as modest as an old shoe. It is his pals who have seen him perform who say he is the top pursuit pilot in the air—any air.

Shortly after the exploit at Vigan, Wagner led a depleted squadron of pursuit planes on what should have been a bombers' job, if the Americans had had any bombers, which they didn't. Three Jap transports were reported about ready to start landing their soldiers ashore. Wagner and his gang of pursuits took off. They had no trouble spotting the transports.

The Americans did not have a bomb in the crowd, so, with Wagner in the lead, they dived low and turned on their machine guns. Down and over, then up and down and over again, the squadron tore across the Japs, the troopships. The boats were not large ones but they were filled to the rails with Japs. That's all Wagner needed to know—that the boats were filled with Japs.

"Kill 'em, kill 'em all!" he shouted as he swept back and forth, spraying the enemy boats each time and with all his gang doing the same. With no Jap planes to prevent them, they kept raining lead into the transports until all three went down, with all they contained. Not an American was lost. Perhaps it was the first time that enemy transports had been sunk by machine gun fire.

A day later Wagner and his crew made another attack on still more transports. This time they had to fight Zeros as well, but in addition to their guns, some of the Americans this time had loaded on a 50-pound bomb apiece, which they carried right in their laps. This was bombing by dead reckoning. Down came the Americans, some shooting guns, others letting go what they had in their laps, heaving the bombs overboard with their hands. It was an odd combination but it did the business. And for cleaning up this job, at least two of the Americans used grenades which they threw as they passed over close. They took terrible effect. "Very nice effect," was the way Wagner put it.

Orders now arrived to break up what was left of the squadron. General MacArthur ordered Wagner and other pursuit fliers to Australia to bring back more planes to the Philip-

Lieutenant Colonel Boyd D. Wagner

pines. The boys went to Australia, but they did not return.
It was too late to help the Philippines. All was over there.
Captain Wagner was ordered to remain in Australia and
start a school for training pursuit pilots.

Buzz Wagner had never done any teaching, although he
had been on the receiving end of a lot of it. Going to the
University of Pittsburgh from his home at Emeigh, Pennsylvania, he studied aeronautical engineering for three years.
He became a flying cadet in 1937 and was graduated from
the Air Corps Primary Flying School, Randolph Field, and
later from the Advanced School at Kelly Field. He got his
commission in June, 1938.

Wagner didn't think he'd like teaching, for he has a
theory about war he was working on; working to prove.
"Pursuit flying is a science," he says, "but once you are in
battle you'll find that instinct plays as big a part as science.
Maybe bigger. You've got to get in there and kill the Jap.
You've got to spread all the death and destruction you can.
There's plenty of it in these American guns. In a war the
side which kills the most men wins. Or, that's my story and
I'm sticking to it."

But Wagner is a good soldier. Into his pursuit school he
is putting everything he's got. Robert Sherrod, correspondent with the American forces in Australia, tells how a part
of Lieutenant Colonel Wagner's curriculum works: A new
squadron of Wagner's pupils were going out from an American airfield in Australia to attack one of the near-by Jap
air bases. Wagner, who was still suffering from a glass
splinter in one eye—the result of a Jap bullet against his
windshield—was not supposed to be doing any flying. But
he is a teacher who believes devoutly in practical demonstra-
tion.

Just before the squadron of green pilots took off, Wagner
leaped into a plane, set her going, and waved for the others
to follow. "Teacher's going, too," he shouted.

Off they went. They found their target and all took a crack at it, including, you may be sure, teacher. They destroyed fifteen Jap planes on the ground. They also shot all hell out of a big gasoline dump at Lae, firing it plenty.

Teacher Wagner was proud of his pupils. He reported they had engaged in some of the darnedest dog fights he had ever seen. "Looking at my boys, all tangled up with Jap Zeros and all firing at once," he said, "reminded me of one big tumbleweed. They fought well, these boys. I'm mighty proud of them."

Lieutenant Colonel Wagner has been telling Americans what the Jap Zero plane is like, what it can do, and what it can't. He told Byron Darnton, war correspondent of the New York *Times*, that the Zero is not a "wonder plane," as has been alleged, but it does have the respect of every pilot who has gone against one. He credited the Zero with being the principal reason the Japs were so successful in pushing so far into the South Pacific so rapidly; Jap air power was much more formidable than anyone but the Japs had expected.

Wagner is no man to warn a pilot to be cautious, but he does believe in letting a man know exactly what he is up against so far as plane performance is concerned. This realistic attitude is perhaps something that not only American pilots but all Americans have lacked in respect to things Japanese. In the past we thought of Japanese manufactures as shoddy stuff—toys, games, machines, light bulbs, clothing, anything, put together with haywire or whatever was the cheapest way. The Japs were making themselves a world power commercially through copying everything made by other nations, but making the copy flimsy, shoddy. Americans and most other nations had come to think of Jap things, anything, as the poorest of poor stuff.

This was true enough of most of their manufactures—

but not of the things they made for war. Wagner could find
no evidence anywhere in Jap aircraft of skimpy material.
The material is thinner than that used in American fighters,
he says, but it is perfectly good duralumin.

In describing the Zero to his pilot pupils Wagner goes
into detail, using planes he and others have shot down in
his classes. "The Zero's wings and fuselage are made in one
piece," he points out. "This means that the Japs can't
change wings if they are damaged, but must replace the
entire job. That system has an advantage in less weight
and in great rapidity of manufacture. But I doubt that
the Japs can make them fast enough. Fact is, I doubt that
even Americans could produce planes fast enough by that
system."

Wagner praises the fine landing gear of the Japs, point-
ing out that it folds all the way up into the fuselage, making it completely smooth on the bottom. The whole ship is
flush-riveted, and there are only a few protuberances, which
makes for small air resistance.

The Zero is equipped with a twin-row radial engine with
fourteen cylinders. It develops from 950 to 1000 horsepower.
The cockpit is roomy. There are two 20-mm. cannon, one in
each wing, and two synchronized 7.7 machine guns that shoot
through the propeller, using grooves in the engine cowling.

On top of the throttle is a lever by which the pilot, with
his left thumb, selects the guns he wants to use. He pushes
forward to fire the machine guns, and in backward position
the pilot can fire both the machine guns and the cannon
simultaneously.

The wings are supported by two spars that are lighter
than the supports used on American fighters. The Zero's
instrument panel is a good one, with nothing unnecessary
and nothing left out. The Zero's canopy, Wagner says, is
as smooth a job as he ever saw; but little consideration is

shown for the pilot. The Zero's pilot has to get along as best he may with no protective armor plate, although this lack may have since been repaired.

At high altitudes the Jap planes perform extremely well because of their light weight and because they are equipped with a supercharger that offsets the effect of thin air on the motor of the engine. The Zero can dive as steeply as our fighters, but ours will pull out of a dive more quickly. Its fire power isn't anywhere near so powerful as ours.

Wagner says he would rather fight in an American than a Jap plane, but he wants his men to know all possible about the enemy ships.

Colonel Wagner knows that pursuit pilots are the rankest kind of individualists. Big bombers carry a crew of nine and the lives of all are dependent on good teamwork. The pursuit pilot flies alone. He must run his plane, fire his guns. His life depends largely on his own skill and instant thinking—thinking that must carry the best of judgment, a mind that must be made up in split-second time.

The average age of Wagner's pursuit-pilot pupils is twenty-three. They love flying. They have to be taught to like killing. Wagner stresses over and over the absolute necessity for a vast desire to kill the enemy. He also stresses his belief that, in battle, good old instinct plays a big part in success or failure. But he tells his boys they've got to learn the science of flying pursuit planes. He tells them that he himself is an engineer; that the engineering training he got at college is priceless to him. He never mentions the Distinguished Service Cross which the Army awarded him for his exploit at Vigan and which the Army insists was "for extraordinary heroism."

He has no doubt about the courage and ability of the young Americans who man most of our pursuit planes, and one of his reasons for this opinion is worth setting down.

"After all," he said, "our boys have more to fight for than anybody else on earth."

Due to the extreme youth of most American pilots, and especially of the youth of at least one American lieutenant colonel of the Air Force, a favorite story in Australia is the one about the sign in a Melbourne pub. "Lieutenant colonels under eighteen years of age," says this sign, according to the gag, "will not be served ales and liquors unless accompanied by their parents."

Buzz Wagner doesn't give a damn what the sign says, and Army men seem to be of the opinion that Wagner's school is turning out some of the finest pursuit pilots that ever flew. "If they are half as good as their teacher," an Air Corps general told this reporter, "then they'll lick all hell out of anybody in the air against them."

"When wounded a second time by two machine gun bullets through his chest, he climbed to the top of a tank, manned its anti-aircraft and fired into strongly held enemy position until knocked off the tank by a third severe wound."

CITING LIEUTENANT WILLIBALD BIANCHI, PHILIPPINE SCOUTS, FOR MEDAL OF HONOR, ON BATAAN, 1942.

16

FIGHTING FILIPINOS

ALTHOUGH NO AMERICAN SOLDIER who fought them forty years ago was left in doubt concerning the courage of the Filipino soldier, comparatively few Americans had any idea about the matter, one way or the other, until the battle on Bataan began in 1942.

Early in that grim, desperate fight against overwhelming odds, a Filipino soldier, Sergeant José Calugas, did something that brought him the first Congressional Medal of Honor to be awarded an enlisted man in the present war. In January of 1942 he was thirty-three years old, pretty old for a soldier, if our Army's way of thinking is correct. But he was a darned good soldier, with reenlistments in the Philippine Scouts running back to 1930 and a character and efficiency rating of excellent.

On the 16th of January his regiment, the 88th Field Artillery, Philippine Scouts, was in a hot sector near Culis, on Bataan Peninsula. His own unit, Battery B, was doing all right that day, and Calugas was performing his regular duties as mess sergeant, paying no heed to the Jap shells bursting in front and rear of his kitchen.

A neighboring battery of his regiment, however, was getting a terrible plastering. While working in the kitchen with his crew, Sergeant Calugas had time and was curious enough to keep an eye on the near-by battery. He saw that one of the gun positions had been well bracketed by Jap artillery, and now the shells were falling true, and deadly. While Calugas watched and listened, he saw a mighty burst fair at the gun, and as the smoke slowly drifted off, he could see the ground littered with men.

Sergeant Calugas watched and listened for one moment more. No movement, no sound came from the battered gun crew. Then Calugas acted.

One of his officers saw him start like a hound and thought him mad. The stocky figure ran like the wind across better than a hundred yards of open ground, while shells burst front and rear, and machine gun bullets whined through the area. The stocky figure dived into a small clump of bushes but did not stop. They saw it emerge, still running like the wind. On and on he went, lost to sight now and again behind the flame-and-dirt spumes of exploding shells. The man was going through a shelling that seemingly a tank could not have passed.

On he went. He reached the gun position unhurt to find all of the cannoneers either dead or so badly wounded they could not stand. The Jap's bracket was still working. Bursts were falling right close.

Taking in the situation at a glance, Calugas ran to a battery fox hole, where other cannoneers were seeking cover from the awful shelling. With a voluble combination of Filipino and English, he roused the men to action. Leading the way himself, they following, he took six men to the gun. Working like ten men, Calugas, who knew something besides his rice and beans, directed the volunteer crew. They drew the wounded to cover. They found ammunition. They opened the breech of the gun, shoved in a gleaming brass shell, then

slammed her home and let her go. The gun bucked and roared, and the first of many shells screamed over to the Japs. The gun and its crew continued to shoot until the cease-firing order was received.

Then Sergeant Calugas, worried that his own battery would be lacking something for supper, returned to his kitchen and his pots and pans, asking the cooks how the stew was doing and if enough coffee had arrived to serve Battery B.

A few weeks later, when he received the first Congressional Medal bestowed on an enlisted man since December 7, 1941, Calugas was highly pleased, and no little surprised. He seemed to be of the opinion that what he had done, while well enough in its way, was just good soldiering. He was sure, though, that his wife, the former Nora Calabaan, and their little son, Noel, would think the medal very nice. In fact, he thought it so himself.

Or take Private Narcisco Ortilano, also of the Philippine Scouts. That is, if you think you could take him.

Eleven Japs attacked the machine gun position which Private Ortilano was manning all alone. He got four with his gun, then it jammed. The Japs were still coming. He drew his pistol and shot five before his ammunition gave out.

Well, that left only two Japs, just a good solid meal for Private Ortilano—if he only had a shooting iron. The two Japs came on in a bayonet charge. Ortilano stood his ground; here was something he was good at, and liked. He grabbed the gun of the nearest Jap and wrested it from him, losing part of a thumb in the process. Then he stabbed the Jap right through the belly, gave the bayonet a practiced twist—like that—and pulled it out. He then took deliberate aim and shot the last Jap.

When help came, his companions found Private Ortilano busy repairing his jammed machine gun in the middle of

eleven dead Japs. His commanding officer thought enough of this exploit to recommend a Distinguished Service Cross, which he received with flustered modesty.

Sergeant Calugas and Private Ortilano were civilized Filipinos. The wild and tough Igorotes, the hillbillies of Luzon, got into the Bataan fighting too. In fact, it would have been futile to try to keep them out of the fighting. Fighting is a thing they like, the way most people like food.

Early in February, during the Bataan battle, a mob of Igorotes came down out of the hills to help the Americans and Philippine Scouts fight the enemy. Most of these recruits had never worn a pair of pants in their lives, and they didn't start now. Some of them had rifles. All carried their native weapon, the big, mean bolo knife.

The wild men appeared just when the Japs were driving hard against American-Filipino lines on the west side of Bataan. They didn't wait for any orders, but rushed right in where there seemed to be the most noise; and they suffered terrible butchery from machine gun fire.

A bit later, American tanks staged a counterattack. The Igorotes were delighted with the clattering, lumbering machines. "Good, good!" they cried. Again in spite of orders, they leaped onto the tanks, bolos over shoulders, and rode into the war in style. They rode into and over Jap positions, shouting loud enough to be heard above the clamor of the tanks. When a tank stalled because of jungle, the wild men leaped to the ground and attacked the forest with their knives, cutting a path for the machines. They liked to pound on the sides of the tanks with their gun butts and knives, to signal the driver inside to speed up, or to turn this way or that.

When the Jap lines broke, the Igorotes were in heaven. They hit the ground and staged some butchery of their

own, shooting a few Japs but killing many more with their bolos.

Then there were the Moros, from the southern Philippine islands. They had had more experience in what is known as "civilized warfare" than the hillbilly Igorotes. They didn't go in for riding tanks bareback into action, but they loved action all the same, especially hand-to-hand fighting, at which they distinguished themselves nobly. American officers have told that a favorite Moro trick was to thrust one shoulder forward to take a Jap's bayonet thrust—in other words to risk an arm—then to grab the bayonet and hold it with the left hand, while the right hand was used for carving up the Jap.

Clark Lee, Associated Press staff writer, who saw the Moros and Igorotes in action, related that often these fighters would report they had killed several hundred Japanese generals. They reported this with such grave good faith that Lee was curious. He discovered it was due to a misunderstanding of Jap insignia.

Jap privates, first class, says Lee, wear two stars, and corporals three stars; but to the wilder breeds of Filipinos, two stars could mean nothing but a major general, three stars a lieutenant general. Hence the hill troops frequently reported the annihilation of large enemy units composed of nothing but generals.

One wonders if the wilder Filipinos are not causing trouble for the Jap administration of the Islands. Both wild and civilized, the natives fought nobly, according to all reports from the front. It cost First Lieutenant Pablo Sapiandante of the Philippine Army his life to win the Distinguished Service Cross; and it went the same way with Lieutenants Baltazar Adona and Gregorio de Gracia, and Corporal Anyres Baldimas, all of the Philippine Army.

As for the Philippine Scouts, as early as May 1, 1942, the United States Army had awarded fourteen Distinguished Service Crosses to Scouts, as well as the Medal of Honor to Sergeant Calugas. The few Americans who saw service on Bataan and have since returned to the United States seem to be of the opinion that the Filipinos earned every medal and cross they have been awarded, including the *two* DSC's that went to the noted Filipino ace, Captain Jesus Villamor, who routed a huge flight of Jap planes, shot down two or more, and still lives.

"How's the fight going?"

17

SEAMAN CULLEN WALKS POST

THERE IS ONE THING about walking post on guard duty: You may be sure most of it will be very dull—endless minutes, timeless hours—with nothing to break the monotony, with the same old sights and sounds, with nothing suspicious to rouse the imagination, a dull lonesomeness with the hot sun, a cold moon, or with fog for companions; but once in a long time you find you are right in the middle of events, even of Events. That is, if you are alert.

Young John Cullen was alert. He had walked hundreds of miles alone on guard duty along the south shore of Long Island, and nothing much had happened. It might have dulled the mind of youngsters less alive that Cullen, a 21-year old seaman of the United States Coast Guard. Then came that foggy night, so filled with Events, in midsummer of 1942.

Seaman Cullen left the Coast Guard station at Amagansett at midnight to start his six-mile patrol along the eastern shore. Visibility was very poor, but Cullen had scarcely made a quarter of a mile when he plainly saw three men.

One was fully dressed in civilian clothing. The other two were in bathing suits and in water up to their knees. Cullen couldn't see what they were doing.

"What's the trouble?" Cullen shouted.

There was no answer, and the stranger on the beach started walking rapidly toward Cullen.

"Who are you?" the Guardsman challenged.

The man kept right on coming. Cullen reached into a pocket for his flashlight. This movement brought a response, as the man slowed his pace.

"Wait, hold on a minute," the stranger cried. "Are you Coast Guard?"

Cullen said he was and repeated his demand: "And who are you?"

"Fishermen, from Southampton. We've run aground."

Cullen couldn't see any fishing boat or any other craft, but he was willing to play. "Come on up to the Station and wait for daybreak," he said.

By now the stranger was only a few feet off. The two other men in bathing suits were wading ashore and were coming up. The fully dressed man spoke to Cullen. "Wait a minute," he said. "You don't know what's going on. How old are you? Have you a father and a mother? Do you want to see them again?" Then he added, "I wouldn't want to have to kill you."

This was sort of tough talk. The other two men were coming up now, one of them dragging a bag. He was talking in what Cullen thought was German.

Might as well make a gag out of it, Cullen thought. He spoke up. "What's in the bag, clams?" Cullen knew there were no clams for miles around.

"Yes, that's right, clams." The fully dressed man spoke. He seemed to be influenced by the Coast Guardsman's apparent gullibility. His voice changed from its hard threatening texture to a friendly tone. "Why don't you forget the

whole thing?" he said. He reached into his pocket. "Here, take this money. One hundred dollars."

"I don't want any money," said Cullen.

The man hauled out a big wallet and fished out another wad of bills. "Here, take this, three hundred dollars, and forget everything."

Cullen was doing himself some thinking, making up his mind in a hurry. "Sure, I'll take the money," he said. "Okay, brother."

The stranger passed him a sheaf of bills. "Now look me straight in the eye," he commanded. Cullen did so, for a full minute, perhaps two minutes, a long time anyway, while the man kept repeating: "Would you recognize me if you saw me again? I say, would you recognize me if you saw me again?"

"No," said Cullen, "I wouldn't."

The man seemed satisfied. Cullen stuffed the money in his pocket, said "So long," and walked away into the fog, taking the same direction he had been moving when he sighted the men. The others silently watched him go.

As soon as he was safely enveloped in the mist, Cullen put on all speed and ran like hell for the Coast Guard Station.

Bosun's Mate Carl R. Jenette was on duty. Cullen told his story hurriedly, about the men, the German talk, the bribe, the implied threats. Jenette telephoned his superiors, Warrant Officer Oden and Chief Bosun Warren Barnes, who were at Barnes' home near by.

Then Jenette gave Cullen a rifle and rounded up three other Guardsmen whom he also armed. All five went on the double to the spot on the beach, less than five minutes' run.

They could not find a sign of a landing on the beach. The sand seemed sheer smooth. "But I know this is the place," Cullen said.

Jenette posted Cullen and two others on guard at the

spot, while he and the other Guardsmen explored the dunes. At about this time Chief Bosun Barnes, a veteran of thirty years in the Guard who had been retired just before Pearl Harbor and re-enlisted immediately after, arrived. As he was running down toward the beach, Barnes noted a rift in the heavy fog, and through the rift he saw a long, thin object, perhaps seventy feet long, about one hundred and fifty feet off shore. At the same time he heard the roar of engines that a moment later became the steady throbbing of Diesel machinery.

Fearing an immediate attack, Barnes disposed his men along the dunes with orders to fire if a landing were attempted. But the fog soon swallowed up the craft, and the noise of the engines receded, then died away.

Up and down the beach the Guardsmen continued their search. Once, on some distant dune, they saw a bright quick light, but nothing was there when they got to the spot, or what they judged was the spot. It was all sort of eerie, and now again came the sound of the chugging engines, loud and strong. The craft seemed to be moving eastward. The noise died away again.

The first alarm given by Cullen had been relayed from the Guard station to Army and Navy headquarters, and before dawn a detachment of soldiers joined the Guardsmen on the beach.

About daybreak Cullen and Barnes found some cigarettes half buried in the sand. They were of German manufacture.

The sun came up, and a little later Guardsman Brooks discovered a furrow, very thin, in the sand, obviously caused by something being dragged. Brooks and another man followed the furrow to a spot in the sand that seemed to be wetter than the surrounding beach—the way freshly disturbed sand looks. And some distance above the tide line near this wet spot was a pair of wet bathing trunks, possibly left as a marker.

Seaman John Cullen, U.S. Coast Guard

Coast Guardsmen poked the sand with a long stick and felt something firm. They went to digging, and a few minutes' work brought forth four boxes.

Meanwhile Barnes found another damp spot. He dug and came up with a mass of German clothing, including two dungaree outfits, a reversible civilian overcoat, overshoes, and an overseas cap. On the cap was a small metal swastika.

All of the finds were taken to the Guard Station. The boxes proved to be of wood bound with marlin that also served to make handles. Guardsmen ripped the wood off one box to find an inner case of tin. Barnes took a can opener and went to work.

One case was filled with pen and pencil sets of a very special sort—not the kind to use lead and ink. A second case was full of loose powder and small glass tubes. In the two cases were the makings of thousands of small and efficient incendiary bombs.

The two opened boxes and the two still unopened were taken to the Barge Office in New York City. The third box was opened here. What it contained the Coast Guard has not seen fit to say. When Guardsmen went to work opening the fourth and last box, it began emitting a hissing sound. What transpired next is best told in a deathless line from the Coast Guard official report.

"It was then suggested," says this report, "that they open it at the end of the pier."

It was done. Lugging the box that was hissing like a crate of cobras, and which for all they knew might contain a large contact bomb, Lieutenant Commander J. A. Glynn and Lieutenants F. W. Nirschel and Sydney K. Franken, took it to "the end of the pier," as suggested, and opened it.

"They discovered," continues the Coast Guard's extremely sluggish report, "that the hissing sound had been caused by the contact of salt water with TNT."

That was how the German saboteur invasion, probably only the first of such, came to light through the alertness of Second Class Seaman John Cullen of Bayside, Long Island, a man who had walked hundreds of miles without seeing anything more interesting than seagulls and horseshoe crabs.

Men of the Federal Bureau of Investigation, as everyone knows, by now, took up the chase from there and rounded up the group that had landed at Amagansett and another group that had come ashore on the coast of Florida. The public was permitted to know that these enemies had been trained in a German school for saboteurs. Some of them were naturalized American citizens. The saboteurs were tried in one of the most secret trials of record.

Even before Guardsmen found the damp spots on the beach and dug up the infernal-machine material, young John Cullen was begging to be relieved of that $300 "bribe" he had taken. He turned the wad of bills over to Chief Bosun Barnes, who counted it before he made out a receipt. It totaled to $260, or just $40 short of the supposed amount. Seaman Cullen, who used to be a delivery boy for a large Manhattan department store, said it was the first time he had been short-changed.

"I only regret that I have but one life to give for my country."

NATHAN HALE, 1776.

18

CAPTAIN KELLY'S LAST FLIGHT

PERHAPS AS EXTRAORDINARY a citation as ever was bestowed on an American hero was that which a President of the United States wrote one day in 1942. It was addressed to "The President of the United States in 1956," and its text was as follows:

"I am writing this letter as an act of faith in the destiny of our country. I desire to make a request which I make in full confidence that we shall achieve a glorious victory in the war we are now waging to preserve our democratic way of life.

"My request is that you consider the merits of an American youth of goodly heritage—Colin P. Kelly 3rd—for appointment as a cadet in the United States Military Academy at West Point. I make this appeal in behalf of this youth as a token of the nation's appreciation of the heroic services of his father who met death in line of duty at the very outset of the struggle which was thrust upon us by the perfidy of a professed friend.

"In the conviction that the service and example of Captain Colin P. Kelly Jr. will long be remembered, I ask for this consideration on behalf of Colin P. Kelly 3rd.— Franklin D. Roosevelt."

A Congressional Medal of Honor, in Captain Kelly's name, already had gone to his parents, and his portrait now hangs in the Academy at West Point.

Young Colin Kelly's fighting days were few, but they were gallant days and his final deed electrified a nation:

The war was merely a few hours old. Japs had attacked Pearl Harbor and were now attacking the Philippines. The Army Air Force squadron, in which Captain Kelly was a pilot, was ordered to bomb an enemy fleet then approaching the Islands. Kelly took off with the others.

Flying fairly high, Captain Kelly came in over the flotilla of Japs, then slanted in a long glide that brought his plane squarely over the biggest ship in the enemy fleet, later identified as the battleship *Haruna*. Kelly's bombardier let go three heavy bombs, the last of which made a direct hit amidships.

Kelly's plane had been under heavy anti-aircraft fire, and now it was attacked by a number of Jap fighter planes. Kelly's ship was soon badly shot up and burning. Captain Kelly ordered his men to bail out, and they went over the side in their chutes. Kelly stayed with his burning ship, which crashed on land not far from Clark Field, killing its pilot.

Fourteen years hence, when Colin P. Kelly 3rd has attained the age qualification for West Point, the name of his father, first Medal of Honor man in World War II, is sure to come up again. But in the meantime it is not likely to be forgotten.

Captain Colin P. Kelly, Jr.

"... he fought a German machine gun battalion single handed, and with the help of seven privates took 132 German prisoners."

CITING SERGEANT ALVIN C. YORK,
MEUSE-ARGONNE, 1918.

19

THEY COME IN ALL KINDS

THERE ARE NO RULES about the making of heroes. They come in all sizes and colors and shapes, from all walks of life, from every stratum, and the things they do in the matter of becoming heroes are as varied as the men themselves.

Circumstances, as many a hero himself has observed, often have a great deal to do with making a hero. But somewhere along the line certain factors are present. Perhaps it is devotion to duty, perhaps it is skill of high degree, and it may be simply courage. Sometimes all three of these as well as other factors are present. They combine with the time, the place, and a man, and a genuine hero is the result.

*　　*　　*

THE MAN WHO GAVE THE WARNING

Not one in ten thousand Americans can name him who at two minutes past seven on the morning of December 7, 1941, was the most important man in all the armed forces of the United States, Army or Navy, at home or abroad.

He was Private Joseph Lockard of the Signal Aircraft Warning Regiment stationed on the Island of Oahu, Territory of Hawaii.

For one brief moment, a moment in which the entire course of war in the South Pacific could have been changed, Private Lockard held the lives of thousands of soldiers and sailors in his hand. And Private Lockard did not fail. He rose to the occasion, and promptly. Fifty full minutes before the attack he warned his duty officer at the information center that a large flight of planes was 132 miles distant and coming in fast. Private Lockard did this immediately and accurately. After that the warning was in other hands, and —were the stars not in the right juxtaposition that day, or was there some invisible shadow cast by the sun that clouded the minds of men in responsible places? Was there a sinister miasma in the air around the Island of Oahu?

Whatever it was, Private Lockard's tremendous warning was in other hands by five minutes past seven, and somewhere along the line, the hands were tragically unequal to the responsibility placed in them.

Fifty minutes after Private Lockard gave the alarm, fifty full precious minutes in which so much could have been done that men have wept to think of it, fifty full minutes later the armada of Japs came in over the mountains to catch the Army and Navy in a condition in which no American forces had been caught before. A week later, after his personal investigation, Secretary of the Navy Knox said as little as possible and that was enough:

"The United States services were not on the alert against the surprise air attack on Hawaii."

The War Department, however, found that at least one man was very much on the alert that morning, and the citation which awarded the Distinguished Service Medal to

Lockard, by then a staff sergeant, on February 10, 1942, carried the official account by Lieutenant General Delos C. Emmons, commanding officer.

This brief account of a prompt and accurate warning of the greatest importance, which went unheeded and with results only too familiar to all Americans, might well be made a piece of required reading for all soldiers, sailors, and Marines in the armed forces of the United States. As General Emmons put it:

"Investigation having been made as required in Army regulation 600-45, I recommend the award of the Distinguished Service Medal to Staff Sergeant Joseph L. Lockard for exceptionally meritorious service in a duty of great responsibility. Sergeant Lockard, then a private, was the operator in charge of the detector unit operated by his organization on the Island of Oahu, Territory of Hawaii, on the morning of Dec. 7, 1941. In order that instruction in the operation of aircraft-warning equipment might be given to another soldier under training, he, in devotion to duty, remained at his station upon completion of the scheduled operating period. At approximately 7:02 A.M. a signal was detected on the instruments, which, in the opinion of Lockard, signified a large number of planes in flight approximately 132 miles distant.

"At that moment Lockard was placed in a position of great and grave responsibility to his country. After rechecking the distance and azimuth, Lockard promptly contacted the duty officer of the information center and furnished him with complete particulars of the readings.

"Subsequent investigations have proven conclusively that the airplanes reported by Lockard were the large Japanese air force which attacked the Island of Oahu at approximately 7:55 A.M."

Elbert Hubbard once wrote a little piece he titled "A

Message to Garcia" about a soldier's devotion to duty. It was far from accurate as to fact, but it told a dramatic story and it became immensely popular, being reprinted in millions of pamphlets and translated into many languages, including the Japanese.

General Emmons's little piece quoted above, though it has more human warmth in it than most citations, is still couched in the dull official language of the Army. Yet it tells a dramatic and tragic story that all Americans, both military and civilian, could well read and remember.

At the same time of the award, General Emmons recommended Lockard, whose hometown is Williamsport, Pennsylvania, for officers' training school. He was brought to the States, completed his course, and in July the gold bars of a second lieutenant were pinned on his shoulders at Fort Monmouth, New Jersey.

*   *   *

BLACK MAN ON A BATTLESHIP

Doris Miller was the first Negro to win the Navy Cross. On the morning of December 7, Miller, dressed in his usual spick and span white, was going about his duties as mess attendant on board a battleship moored in Pearl Harbor when the alarm sirens sounded.

Men rushed to their battle stations. Then the bombs began dropping. The big ship shuddered from near-misses, and when a big slug hit her fair, she bounced and threw men flat on their faces, some with broken bones.

It wasn't very long before the ship was afire—afire and starting to sink. Doris Miller, tall, black, and handsome in his white clothes, ran up to the deck and on up to the captain's bridge. What was he doing there? The Navy never said. Perhaps Miller was taking food to the captain, but it seems unlikely. One can't know.

Anyway, when Doris Miller got to the bridge the Japs were bombing all hell out of the ship. Bombing and strafing, for machine gun bullets were sweeping the decks. The captain fell flat on the bridge, mortally wounded.

Miller ran to the captain's side. He picked him up in his strong arms and with the help of an officer carried him to a place of comparative safety. It was too late, anyway, but Doris Miller didn't know that.

Now Miller went back to the bridge. There was a machine gun there and no one was manning it. Miller knew how to operate a gun. He stepped up and grabbed the handle. Just then a flight of Jap strafers was coming in, very close. Miller tilted his gun just right and set her going. He shot at the Japs and hit them, and he continued to shoot until an officer ordered him from the bridge.

Said Secretary Knox's recommendation of the sharecropper's son of Route 1, Box 339, Waco, Texas:

"For distinguished devotion to duty, extraordinary courage and disregard of his own personal safety . . . While at the side of his Captain on the bridge, Miller, despite enemy strafing and bombing and in the face of serious fire, assisted in moving his Captain, who had been mortally wounded, to a place of greater safety, and later manned and operated a machine gun until ordered to leave the bridge."

Admiral Chester W. Nimitz himself was pleased to pin the Cross on Doris Miller's jacket.

* * *

PRINCE OF THE SHUTTLE SERVICE

In all of his many flights, flights the like of which few veteran fliers have known, young Lieutenant Theodore John Boselli never once came in contact with an enemy plane, yet the Army was happy to hang a Distinguished Flying Cross on him. His career with the Ferrying Command certainly called for some recognition, and in May of 1942, when they managed to ground him long enough for the ceremony, he got the recognition.

Boselli, a native New Yorker, had never been in a plane in his life until he enlisted in the Army Flying Corps almost two years to a day before he stood up straight to get his medal. He proved to be quick to learn, a youngster of twenty-four who was not only fearless but also had the cool judgment of a veteran flier. So they gave him a commission and a job in the Ferrying Command.

Boselli was good. He was awfully good. Before our part of the war began, he had navigated one of the ships in the first mass flight of bombers from the United States to Honolulu. He charted the course taken by the second experimental flight of the Ferrying Command to England, and did it so well he was put in as pilot of one of the two planes that carried the W. Averell Harriman party to Moscow.

All that totaled some 100,000 air miles of flying before we got into the war. Then Lieutenant Boselli's real work began.

First off, he flew William C. Bullitt on a diplomatic mission to Africa and the Near East. Boselli expected to be back in Miami for Christmas, but instead he was in Darwin, Australia. From here he started what came to be known as the Red Cap, or Shuttle, or Porter Service, running back and forth from Rangoon to Bandung, to Surabaya, to Calcutta, to Melbourne, and many way points.

On these flights he outguessed or outmaneuvered the Japs and the Germans, never once coming in contact with the enemy. His passenger list read like a Who's Who of Allied commanders and included at one time or another General George H. Brett, General Lewis H. Brereton, and General Sir Archibald P. Wavell. General Douglas MacArthur was just about the only big brass hat Boselli missed.

In mid-February, when the battle of Java was rapidly

being lost by the Allies, Boselli was ordered to help with the evacuation of that island. He made four round trips from Australia, avoiding all Jap warships and planes, then thick over Java as hornets around a hive, and was not even seen by enemy patrols.

Boselli's favorite plane, a Consolidated B-24, was the one he had on two of his most trying and exciting flights. The first one was in late January, when he flew to the Philippines to bring out twenty-five much needed ground-crew sergeants. To accomplish this he had to avoid the scores of Jap planes on patrol around the Islands, and he had to make his Philippine landing on an unlighted field on a very dark midnight. On this flight he was obliged to change course four times, and wound up by relying on the stars to guide him.

What he terms his next to most nerve-racking flight was on April 28, 1942. He had just arrived in Australia from one of his ferrying trips to India. Orders came to fly at once to the Philippines to rescue thirty officers and men who had escaped from Bataan.

Boselli took the big bomber aloft, swung her around, and started in broad daylight on the 1,800-mile voyage. His combat equipment was very light; almost any enemy fighter could have caught up with the heavy ship and shot it down without trouble.

But Boselli knew his airways. He plowed on through the waning day, not once coming in sight of enemy plane or ship, and just at dusk brought his plane down on Philippine soil. His passengers were waiting. One of them was a dark, stocky chap, Lieutenant John D. Bulkeley, who had been making some history with his torpedo boats and was soon to be much in the news.

Packing thirty-seven, instead of thirty, men into the B-24 proved to be quite a task and called for some careful figuring and stowing away. But it was done, and away the plane went, back to Australia, packed, as Lieutenant Boselli says, like an IRT subway train. It arrived, said the official report, "without incident."

This flight was completed on April 29, 1942, and Boselli calculated it brought his total flying mileage, in a little less than two years, to the good round figure of 250,000 air miles. At the ripe age of twenty-six he had flown more miles than many veteran Air Corps pilots.

*   *   *

The "Heron" Incident

With characteristic reserve the Navy referred to it as the "USS *Heron* Incident." Impartial observers, of which there were none, might have called it a battle. It lasted seven hours, longer than many battles, and the wonder of it was not the courage of the Americans—one commodity of which the United States has plenty—but that the little *Heron* and most of her crew survived so determined an assault by overwhelming forces.

The USS *Heron* was and doubtless still is, if Lieutenant Kabler is still on her bridge, a small seaplane tender. She is not a fighting ship, although she carries an anti-aircraft battery and machine guns.

One day in January, the first January of America's participation in the war, the *Heron* was steaming along in South Pacific waters, going about her business of tending seaplanes. Lieutenant William L. Kabler, thirty-three years old, of Bristol, Virginia, was on the bridge. He sighted far-off specks that presently became a full-fledged flight of Jap bombers, big four-engined flying boats. Kabler sent his men to battle stations, then counted the coming planes. There were ten of them. Kabler prepared to maneuver his ship; it was the only way he could hope to escape total destruction.

On came the Japs. They stayed fairly high at first, letting go a score of 100-pound bombs at the only vessel in sight, the *Heron*. Under the orders of Lieutenant Kabler, who was obviously a very skillful man with a ship, the little tender zigged to port, then to starboard. Bomb splashes edged her on both sides. Two came mighty close, close enough to rock the *Heron* almost out of the water. But her sides were stout, and her seams were holding so far.

The Japs circled leisurely, then came back, this time much lower, and the *Heron*'s anti-aircraft opened up. Just about then a bomb struck fair in the middle of the *Heron*'s foredeck. She bounced clean up out of the sea, and for a moment her commander and crew thought the blow might be mortal, but Kabler never once left her bridge where bomb fragments were hitting all over.

When the smoke had cleared and the flames had been put out, Kabler found his boat still moving. Her engines and steering gear were unimpaired. Her guns were still shooting.

Presently the flying boats came back, this time with five more planes, land-based bombers. The new bombers came over first and all dropped a stick of bombs. None were even near-misses, so skillfully was the *Heron* maneuvering. Then the flying boats dropped another load—not a hit or a near-miss in the lot. All went wide—or wide enough.

The planes circled around, and the land-based bombers came down low and ran in with their machine guns open. If they couldn't sink this tin-pot vessel with bombs, they would shoot her under with gun fire. The *Heron*'s gunners stood up to the murderous attack and kept their own guns hot, setting one of the attackers on fire.

The little ship was meanwhile running a ragged course, turning on her beam, almost heeling over at every turn, and dodging, dodging.

The Japs went away again, this time for perhaps half

an hour, and Kabler wondered if they had gone into conference. Then they came back. This time it was to be torpedoes. Up there on his bridge, Lieutenant Kabler saw the first plane drop low, then come in full speed and heave the torpedo. Kabler put his rudder hard left, and turned on a dime. The missile passed.

The second plane came in, the tin fish leaped out and started spinning. Kabler put his helm way over. The second tube missed. So did the third, by a few yards.

The torpedo planes went away. The straight bombers came over again, lower than before, and the *Heron* turned its guns on them. On deck Lieutenant Franklin D. Buckley of Philadelphia, executive officer, was directing the *Heron's* anti-aircraft, and Chief Bosun William Harold Johnson, of Chula Vista, California, was all over the craft, watching everything. The gunners were getting the range. They plastered one of the big ships fair. She blew up into flames, then fell headlong into the sea. They hit another of the flying boats, and saw it pull out of formation and go away over the horizon, still smoking.

The remaining attackers dropped half a dozen more sticks, went away, and came back to drop more, while the *Heron's* guns were red hot from steady shooting.

But the attack was petering out. Fifteen planes had failed to sink, or even to damage seriously the one small vessel. The *Heron*, with Kabler on her bridge, a place his men say he never once left, steamed into her home base under her own power. She was battered and leaking, but all in one piece. One may call it a miracle, but the *Heron's* crew don't believe in miracles. They say it was due to the skillful seamanship of Lieutenant Kabler.

Lieutenant Commander Kabler had earned his promotion and the Navy Cross they gave him. A Navy Cross also went to Chief Bosun Johnson "for heroic conduct under fire," and another Cross to Machinist's Mate Robert L. Brock,

Duquoin, Illinois, for "extreme disregard of personal safety."

At last report the seaplane tender *Heron* was still carrying on its business of tending seaplanes, which is a pretty fine record for a ship that has been through an "incident."

* * *

ESCAPE IN THE JUNGLE

Sometimes it is the aftermath of battle that fighting men will remember longer than the battle itself.

Lieutenant Louis W. Ford and his crew of an Army bomber had just hit the Japs at Rabaul hard. They put the stuff right down on the target. And the Japs hit back with anti-aircraft fire.

Flying to get away through the hundreds of bursts the American plane was hit again and again. First, one engine was put out of commission. Then in short order a propeller was damaged, the hydraulic lines were shot up so they wouldn't work, the interphone was cut in two, the wide-open bomb-bay wouldn't close, and one wing was turning to shreds.

Lieutenant Ford knew he would have to land somewhere and before very long. Rabaul and New Britain below him were strictly Jap territory. If the plane would hold together and fly, he might bring her down in New Guinea, across the strait. He laid his course out over the water.

He tried for a little more altitude, but the plane was too far gone; just holding what he had would be lucky enough. Dropping a few more feet every mile, dropping steadily but still making good headway, the plane got across the water. Now they were over land. Ford and his crew looked for somewhere to ground. They knew there was no airfield in the region, but they soon sighted what looked to be a fairly level spot, miles back from shore—how many miles they were to judge later.

The level-looking spot was entirely surrounded by trees and jungle. It wasn't the spot a man would pick under ordinary circumstances, but the plane was now on its last lap. Ford could tell by the way she behaved.

"Prepare for crash landing," he shouted as loud as he could, then banked to come in against the wind.

Lieutenant Ford did a pretty good job, everything considered. The ship came down with a bump that jarred everybody and one wing wrapped itself around a big tree, let go, and the plane skidded some three hundred feet to a stop. Nobody was hurt, just shaken a bit.

The crew crawled out of the plane. With Ford, who was twenty-two years old and from Los Angeles, were Lieutenants Arthur E. Andres, twenty-three, Newton, Massachusetts; John Disbro, Defiance, Ohio; and Edward H. Ashley of San Antonio, Texas; and Privates Robert Long, Centerburg, Ohio; J. E. Ochs, Lancaster, Pennsylvania; J. A. Roberts, Kingston, Pennsylvania; and William Lorancer of Saginaw, Michigan. These men may in years to come forget many of their countless flights in bombers, but not one will forget the land trip they were soon to have.

Night came down rapidly. They looked at the forbidding jungle on all sides of the deserted clearing and decided to stay where they were until morning.

It turned out to be a horrible night. Mosquitoes such as none of the men had ever seen, nor in such myriads, attacked them. Nobody of course had brought along mosquito netting. Even the smokes they made had little effect on the pests. There was no sleep that night.

In the morning Ford, Disbro, and Long set out to find a village, or a river, or something or somebody who or which could tell them how to get home, or out of this place, anyway. The other men remained with the plane.

The three Americans hardly had left the open space when they found the going very soft underfoot. Pretty soon they were sinking into ground and water above their knees. They kept on and in places had to wade through water breast-high, meantime holding their small arms high in the air and meantime, too, wondering what sort of reptiles beneath the murky waters might take a fancy to them.

Coming out of the bog they found a sort of path, much overgrown but still a path, and along this they made a slow journey. At one point they nearly ran into a thing hanging down from a limb across the path. It jerked to sudden life, and the men saw it was a python fifteen feet long. Ford shot it, and for the remainder of the way all hands kept a sharp watch.

Finally they came to a river and were lucky to find a native canoe with no owner around. They got in and floated with the current, while crocodiles flopped and swam to port and starboard. The boys argued as to which was the worse companion, a crocodile or a python. Late that afternoon the canoe and the current brought them to a village, the population of which they later judged to be about one hundred.

"We were sure scared of those natives," Disbro said afterward, "but we soon learned they were even more frightened of us. Seems they recently had had a fight with a neighboring village and thought we were white authorities who had come to punish them.

"We told them we were English—a word we had heard was one they would understand. They did, and they were most kindly after they got over their first fright. They gave us a hut to stay in, and coconuts, bananas, and papaws to eat. When we wanted to sleep at night, there were ten or a dozen of the natives who would not leave our hut. When I dozed off they were still standing there, silent and grinning."

Next day, Ford with the help of two natives made his way back to the crew in the clearing. They were suffering tortures from mosquito bites from which they bled all over. Ford and his crew salvaged all carriable instruments, then blew up the plane, much to the delight of the two natives.

Back again at the village, the Americans remained for eight days, being a continuous free show for the natives who never once ceased their good efforts to make the strangers as comfortable as possible.

Where to go, was the question. None of the natives could speak or understand more than a few words of English, so now began a conference that under other and happier circumstances would have been a scene of high comedy. First, Ford would tackle the job of trying to make clear they were foreigners who wanted to get to a British post or village or camp. He'd talk in short sentences, wave his arms, point this way and that, and perform what he thought was an excellent pantomime of a man who wanted to get to a British camp.

Meanwhile, the head man of the village and all of his councilmen and wives, along with several children, would watch and listen as gravely as judges. When Ford was through, the natives would discuss the matter, then the chief would make some signs of his own and a speech to boot. When he stopped and seemed to be awaiting a reply, Disbro or one of the others would take up from there, going on with such new signs as they could think of. Finally, the natives all began talking at once. The head man or chief then took a stick and started making maps on the ground; he'd draw a few lines in the earth, then give a short speech. The Americans watched and listened open-mouthed. The chief drew more lines, he made motions like paddling a canoe, he grunted a good deal, then made as if eating, and at last as if sleeping.

This seemed to clear up everything in the minds of the other villagers. The chief gave a few orders. Men and women began lugging food to a large canoe near by, the chief made another speech and led the Americans to the boat. With the entire population waving and shouting, the Americans got in and started downstream, with little idea of where it would take them.

Navigating the river proved a slow and ticklish job. There were rapids, and even falls, which they had to carry around. In places crocodiles were so thick as to all but stop progress of the boat. At least three of the crew were keeping watch of things that hung down over the water; they remembered their first python.

All were getting sick. Malaria had laid its hand on them. Ulcers were showing up on skins, along with a continuous series of insect bites. Dysentery was affecting most of the party. The voyage slowed almost to a stop at every carry-around.

After many days and nights that seemed to run together like an endless and horrible dream, the half-mad Americans noted that the river was coming out of the thick jungles and approaching tidewater. Soon they got sight of what they thought must be a British government station. Before they reached it a Jap bomber came over, spotted the big canoe, and let go a couple of bombs. They weren't even near-hits, and the party continued on to the station, which proved to be what they had hoped.

By now they really were ill, but the station had quinine and other medicines for the many things they were suffering from, and good food. And one day late in May of 1942 an American destroyer came and took them to Port Moresby, New Guinea, where they were put away in a hospital to recuperate from malaria.

*   *   *

DOCTOR SEAGRAVE AND NURSES

Often a hero appears who has never had a gun or a grenade in his hand.

Doctor Gordon S. Seagrave, Rangoon-born American Baptist Missionary, was a goiter specialist in Burma. In charge of the Harper Memorial hospital at Namkham, he had established mobile units which cruised the Southern Shan States, aiding natives too ill to be brought to the hospital or to one of the small local dispensaries he had established. He knew the country, spoke the language, loved the people. By the thousands of Burmese to whom he had administered, Doctor Seagrave was considered little short of a god.

Doctor Seagrave might easily have sat out the war in his hospital, but he was still an American in spite of the place of his birth. And when the Chinese came in to defend Thailand and Indo-China from the flooding Japs, he knew he was a missionary doc no longer but an Army man, in fact if not in uniform. He promptly placed all his facilities at the disposal of Chiang Kai-shek and immediately established a medical and surgical setup just behind the Chinese front lines.

Then the Japs attacked further south, in the Karen States near Toungoo, leaving Doctor Seagrave's hospitals without a front. The doctor at once offered his services to Lieutenant General Joseph W. Stilwell in command of the American forces in Burma. They were accepted and the doctor was commissioned a major in the Army Medical Corps.

The fighting around Toungoo came very suddenly. Taking sixteen of his nurses, two jeeps, and eight members of the Friends (Quakers) Ambulance Corps, Doctor Seagrave moved quickly behind the American-Chinese front at Toungoo. The fighting was fierce. Casualties were coming in before the doctor got his operating case open. He had a fair stock of medicines but no other doctor to help him. During the heat of the first fighting he worked one twenty-four-hour stretch in which he cared for one hundred and fifty casualties, some of them pretty bad. His only assistant at this time was Makio, his head nurse, a native Burmese woman who weighed almost one hundred pounds.

Operating on the porch of a house, their work illuminated by the flames of bombed Myinmana, Seagrave and Makio handled the cases, one after the other. The nurse operated on twenty of the minor cases—and minor in that place did not necessarily mean simple—herself.

The attack on Toungoo had come so swiftly that the Chinese had no time to make provision for anything except first aid. Their practice was to send all casualties back to a collecting station where they were given first aid. Then the worst cases were hurried on to Doctor Seagrave in a Friends truck.

For two weeks on the Toungoo front Seagrave and little Makio worked alone, save for the assistance of the Burmese nurses. All of these were young girls who had been trained in Seagrave's hospital and their loyalty in this horrible time was inspiring to Americans and Chinese alike. They averaged a little under five feet tall, and one hundred pounds was reckoned a normal weight. But they were as tough as steel. They stood up under the hardship and unlimited duty without a complaint. They not only nursed the casualties but acted as stretcher bearers when no other help was available. They kept their living quarters policed spick and span, and somehow found time to do the laundry and to keep the improved surgical equipment properly sterilized.

During that first twenty-four-hour hitch of steady operating on the porch, the Japs came over, right over, with their bombers . . .

When the bombers had passed there were more casualties, many from very near the hospital. Seagrave kept four oper-

ating tables going at once, with the nurses finishing the operations after he had done the most essential part.

From a goiter specialist in peacetime to an Army surgeon
in the middle of the war was a leap Doctor Seagrave had to
make almost overnight, and the record indicates he made
the leap with ability, even to the extent of brain surgery.
Of an early casualty he said:

"This man had a bullet enter the top of his head and go
three inches into his brain. I trephined a huge opening in
the skull, opened up the dura mater, washed out a lot of
shattered brains, and put in a vaseline gauze drain. That
night we had to move him along with us to a bungalow on a
hill. Every time the bombers came over, this patient got up
and ran half a mile. After five days, during which he had
no fever and was walking around everywhere—drain out—
we sent him back."

Just when the fighting and the casualties were thickest,
Doctor Seagrave received a couple of most welcome aids,
Captain Donald M. O'Hara, a dentist of the Army Medical
Corps, and Captain John Grindlay, an abdominal surgeon
of the Army who had been stationed at Chungking. O'Hara
didn't claim to be anything but a dentist, but he went to
work like a veteran at the ticklish business of probing for
bullets and shell fragments; and he also had many oppor-
tunities to practice head and jaw reconstruction. It was a
mighty fine place for that.

Grindlay cared for such abdominal wounded as got to him
—and many other wounded too—but most of those wounded
in the stomach died before arrival. Grindlay found Seagrave's nurses—he had Koi and Myang Lewi and Maru
Bauk—for aids and he has since said that he never had
seen such well-trained and willing nurses.

But Burma was playing out fast. A falling back became
a retreat, and the retreat became faster and faster. Finally,
when it was decided to abandon Burma, Doctor Seagrave and

his crew started off with General Stilwell's few troops. They drove about 150 miles in jeeps and trucks, then had to abandon them hurriedly. Orders were to take only what could be carried in the hand, for the way ahead was long and likely to be dreary and hard.

Seagrave and his nurses each took some piece of first-aid equipment or supplies; some took a sheet, others blankets. Then they walked up over 7,000-foot mountains and down the other side. Malaria attacked them. The heat was terrible, even to Burmese. For four days they walked down the middle of a stream, developing sores and blisters. They next had three days on rafts thrown together of bamboo, which floated not on top of the water but a few inches beneath it.

Only dribbles of information have come out of India about that terrible retreat of a few Americans, Burmese, and Chinese, but there has been enough to indicate it to have been one of the most horrible experiences of the war. When the party reached India, they were in need of considerable attention themselves.

* * *

Sergeant Hayes's First Flight

Quite likely Master Sergeant Harry M. Hayes was the only American Army man left on Java. Due to some miscue somewhere along the line, he was left behind when his outfit, an Army Corps unit, pulled out for Australia, just ahead of the Japs.

Hayes is a big, soft-spoken Texan, with a wife and two children in San Antonio, and he had never worried a great deal about anything during his sixteen years in the Air Corps.

He didn't worry now, even with Jap planes flying all over the neighborhood, but was hanging around a Java airport, as he said, "waiting for something to happen," when an American volunteer flier of the Chinese Air Force came up.

"Is there any chance of getting out of here?" the flier wanted to know. "I have my wife with me, and it's going to get tough here in a few days, maybe a few hours."

"Well," said Sergeant Hayes, "we can take a look at the junk left in this airport and see if there's anything that can be made to fly. I don't fly myself. I just fix planes."

Hayes and the flier looked around. They found four wrecked American planes—one B-18 and three Flying Fortresses. These had been left behind by the Americans and they looked pretty much like a junk yard. But Hayes reckoned as to how he might patch up the B-18. The man from China said he couldn't do anything with a Fortress but he could fly a B-18 all right.

Hayes went to work on the plane selected. In a couple of days, during which stray American civilians, with their wives and children, showed up at the airport in the desperate hope there might be some way to get out of Java, Hayes had got the plane into what he believed was workable shape. Everybody concerned had watched the progress of repairs with plenty of interest, and when Hayes said the thing was ready to go, a dozen Americans were on hand ready to board the plane.

But they never got in. The Japs, who had been operating for several days in the general neighborhood, now came over with both bombers and fighters. They had nothing to contend with, and they flew in to bomb and strafe the field, while everybody took to cover.

When the smoke cleared, it was found that the B-18 was a mass of wreckage, blown to pieces.

But the Flying Fortresses were untouched—which still left them in pretty bad shape. Hayes looked them over. "This one might be made to fly a piece," he said, "if we stripped the other two and patched her up." Then he moved his tools into the Fortress. He rounded up a crew of sixty Hollanders and started in.

Hayes lived in that plane for five days, and if he got any sleep none of the Hollanders or the waiting Americans knew of it. He set the Dutch to work in three shifts, twenty men to a shift, and Hayes was foreman all the time. Two engines had to be almost completely rebuilt. The wings had to be repaired. The bomber's tail, badly blasted in some past fight, had to be overhauled.

What bothered Hayes most was how to lessen the weight and to make room enough for the party, which had now grown to seventeen. "Got to take them all," Hayes said. He had everything not absolutely necessary thrown out—the parachutes, the rubber boats, the radio, everything that didn't have a part in making the plane go.

The flier from China had never flown a Fortress, and apparently he didn't want to try. Anyway, Hayes, who had never flown anything, was willing—if the rest were. "All aboard that's going aboard," he said, and seventeen Americans piled in with him.

Well, the engines grunted a few times, then warmed up and the propellers spun, faster and faster. Hayes, the first-time pilot, was at the controls. He started her down the field, made a turn-around, then headed back. Smoke caused by Jap bombs could be seen just over a near-by hill. Hayes prayed to Sam Houston the Japs wouldn't bother to return to the wrecked airport just then. He ran his plane up the field for all she had, and lifted her nose.

The heavily loaded ship left the ground, her engines now throbbing in rhythm. "We're going to Australia," said Sergeant Hayes.

All Hayes knew about Australia was that they had kangaroos there, and it was somewhere to the southeast. He had no chart, no map of any kind. So he just headed her southeast and let it go at that.

Hayes soon discovered that 3,000 feet was going to be tops, and two or three times, when the plane faltered, he thought he couldn't even hold that altitude. But she held at 3,000 feet and Pilot Hayes took her 1,300 miles nonstop and let her down—without flaps—on one of Australia's best airfields. Not a passenger suffered more than a mild bump.

Lee Van Atta, the well-known correspondent, first told the story of Sergeant Harry Hayes's mechanical genius and determined courage. Van Atta said that when United States Army Air officers inspected the plane after its arrival they pronounced it absolutely useless and unfit to go into the air. It was dismantled on the spot.

When last heard from, Sergeant Hayes was carrying on in spite of a broken arm, suffered in a plane crash during operations in Australia. He reckoned, however, that he would soon be out and doing again.

* * *

THESE ARE BRAVE MEN

Thus it is that you can never tell a hero by looking at him. His age doesn't count. He may never get a medal. You can't tell him by the job he holds. He may be a ground mechanic, a cook, a doctor, or the pilot of a fighter plane. He may not be a man at all, but a woman.

Of one thing, though, we Americans may be pretty certain, and that is the quality of our fighting men who bore the brunt of the first fierce fighting, the fighting that was against terribly great odds in men and equipment. These odds are changing rapidly and soon, one hopes, they will be so changed that the courage of our soldiers and sailors will be backed up by preponderance of men and equipment. When that day comes, as it assuredly will, our fighting men will be just as brave and with their new power will bring the war to the conclusion that no real American has ever doubted for a moment.

But as the new heroes are decorated, let us not forget the boys who fought with what they had long before the United States was ready to fight at all. They were gallant men, every one, medals or no, and none will ever be more courageous.

*"Though wounded in the thigh, he retained charge of his boat,
and when the staff was shot away, held the stump in his hand,
with the flag, until we got alongside the* Freeborn."

CITING CAPTAIN-OF-THE-MAINTOP JOHN WILLIAMS,
FIRST NAVAL AWARD OF THE MEDAL OF HONOR,
MATTHIAS POINT, VIRGINIA, JUNE 26, 1861.

20

WHAT THE MEDALS MEAN

THE FIRST AWARD of a decoration to an American fighting man was voted by the Continental Congress in session on March 25, 1776, to General George Washington, and in these words:

"That the thanks of this Congress, in their own name, and in the name of the United Colonies, whom they represent, be presented to his Excellency and soldiers under his command, for their wise and spirited conduct in the siege and acquisition of Boston; and that a medal be struck in commemoration of this great event, and presented to his Excellency; and that a committee of three be appointed to prepare a letter of thanks, and a proper device for the medal."

This was done. Ten years later Congress voted that "the Chevalier John Paul Jones" be awarded a medal of gold for "the valor and brilliant services of that Officer in the command of a squadron of French and American ships . . . etc."

But the young Republic was chary of medals and decorations of all kinds, holding them to have the flavor of monarchy. It was not until 1861, when in December Congress

authorized a Medal of Honor for "such petty officers, sea-
men, landsmen and marines who should distinguish themselves by their gallantry in action and other seamanlike
qualities," that heroism was officially recognized. A similar
award was provided for enlisted men of the Army in July
of 1862.

It will be noted that neither the Navy nor Army provided
for any award to officers. This condition held until as late
as 1915, when award of the Medal of Honor was authorized
for officers as well as enlisted men. Thus, Rear Admiral
Richmond Pearson Hobson, who distinguished himself at
Santiago, Cuba, on June 3, 1898, did not receive a Medal
of Honor until seventeen years afterward. Several other
officers of Spanish-American, and even of Civil War days,
were similarly decorated after many years.

Campaign ribbons and medals have been awarded officers
and men who served in the Civil War, in the various Indian
wars, the Spanish-American War, the Boxer Uprising, the
Philippine Insurrection, the Pacification of Cuba, the Mexi-
can Border troubles just before World War I, and for
World War service, and in various minor expeditions. The
layman should understand that these campaign medals have
nothing to do with heroism, although the wearers of them
may well have been heroes.

American decorations are something else again. They may,
like the Distinguished Service Medal, mean that the wearer
performed duties of grave responsibility with great credit
to himself; or they may, like the Distinguished Service Cross,
signify that the wearer performed some heroic feat "against
an armed enemy."

*   *   *

ARMY DECORATIONS

In 1942 seven decorations for gallantry in action or distinguished service are authorized to be awarded to officers

and enlisted men of the Army. In order of rank, the colors of the ribbon by which they are suspended, and the qualifications for their award, are as follows:

1. The Medal of Honor. A blue field with thirteen stars. This is awarded in the name of Congress to each person who, while an officer or enlisted man of the Army, in action involving actual conflict with an enemy, distinguishes himself conspicuously by gallantry and intrepidity at the risk of his life above and beyond the call of duty. In order to justify an award of the Medal of Honor an officer or enlisted man must perform in action a deed of personal bravery or sacrifice above and beyond the call of duty, so conspicuous as clearly to distinguish him for gallantry and intrepidity above his comrades, involving risk of life or the performance of more than ordinarily hazardous service, the omission of which would not justly subject him to censure for shortcoming or failure in the performance of his duty.

2. The Distinguished Service Cross (dates from 1918). Blue-centered ribbon, red and white edged. This is awarded to persons who, while serving in any capacity with the Army, distinguish themselves by extraordinary heroism in connection with military operations against an armed enemy.

3. The Distinguished Service Medal (dates from 1918). White-centered ribbon, red-edged, with blue pin stripe separating red from white portions. This is awarded to persons who, while serving in any capacity with the Army, distinguish themselves by exceptionally meritorious service to the government in a duty of great responsibility.

4. The Silver Star (dates from 1935). Ribbon striped as follows: narrow blue, narrow white, broad blue, broad white, broad red, broad white, broad blue, narrow white, narrow blue. This is awarded to each person who, while an officer or enlisted man of the Army, is cited for gallantry in action in orders issued from the headquarters of a United States force commanded by or which is the appropriate command of

a general officer, which citation does not warrant the award of the Medal of Honor or the Distinguished Service Cross.

5. The Purple Heart (first instituted in 1782, later allowed to lapse, then re-established in 1932). A purple ribbon edged with gray. This is presented to officers and men of the Army for meritorious service and/or wounds honorably received in action.

6. The Soldier's Medal (dates from 1926). Blue-edged ribbon with thirteen stripes of alternate red and white in center. This is awarded to all members of the Army who have distinguished themselves by heroism not involving actual conflict with an enemy.

7. The Distinguished Flying Cross (dates from 1926). Ribbon striped as follows—blue, white, blue, white, red, white, blue, white, blue. This is awarded to any person who, by serving in any capacity with the Air Corps of the Army, subsequent to April 6, 1917, shall distinguish himself by heroism or extraordinary achievement while participating in an aerial flight. A Bronze Oak Cluster shall be awarded to an officer or enlisted man who performs an act for which he should receive a second decoration of this kind.

*   *   *

Navy Decorations

The Navy, which includes the Marines and Coast Guard, gets along with four decorations for gallantry in action or distinguished service, as follows:

1. The Medal of Honor, with a ribbon similar to that of the Army's Medal, has a slightly different set of qualifications. It is given in the name of Congress to any person who, while in the naval service of the United States, shall, in action involving actual conflict with the enemy, distinguish himself conspicuously by gallantry and intrepidity at the risk of his life above and beyond the call of duty and without detriment

to the mission of his command or to the command to which he is attached.

2. The Distinguished Service Medal (dates from 1918). Blue ribbon with one yellow stripe down center. Qualifications same as for the Army's Distinguished Service Medal.

3. The Navy Cross (dates from 1919). Blue ribbon with one white stripe down center. This is awarded to any person who, while in the naval service, shall distinguish himself by extraordinary heroism or distinguished service in the line of his profession, such heroism not being sufficient to justify the award of the Medal of Honor or the Distinguished Service Medal.

4. The Distinguished Flying Cross is identical with that of the Army, both in appearance and in the matter of award.

11.3479